Rivers of Time

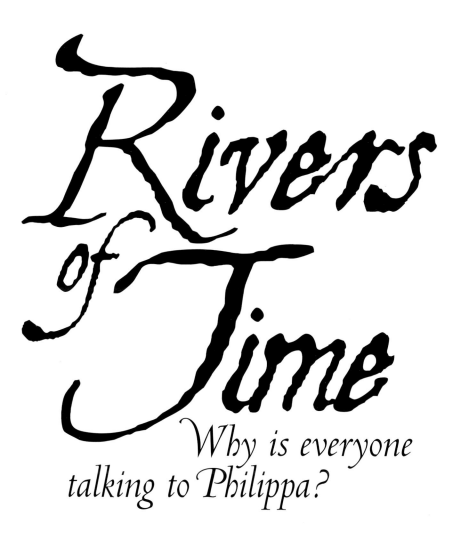

Rivers of Time

Why is everyone talking to Philippa?

June Goodfield

This is a haunting story which touches life at many points. It is a biography, pieced together from painstaking research to reveal the fortunes of one woman on her journey from poverty in Devon to the challenges of a new life across the ocean.

But it is also an autobiography. The author's love of the island and its people, her powerful need to resurrect the unknown and long-buried Philippa, together with her determination and tenacity in creating a life and character from a mere handful of facts, make compulsive reading. It may be, as she herself suggests, that she needed this all-compelling pursuit at a very difficult time of her own life. Biography, autobiography, history, this is a moving story, beautifully told.

Edna Healey

Fiction can often breathe life into a by-gone time far more vividly than academic history and with *Rivers of Time* June Goodfield has done that superbly. Starting with only a name and date on a 17th century tombstone in a beautiful, isolated spot on Nevis and, combining diligent research with a perceptive understanding of a people and a country she knows well, the author has solved a mystery that for years has puzzled many people.

Based on true facts, this is a romantic and inspiring tale of a dirt-poor English woman and how she came to a live and die in a place as foreign to her as another planet. There, triumphing over danger and adversity, she helped lay the foundations of the present day Caribbean society. Anyone who visits or lives in the West Indies should read this book. I wager that they will love it – as I do.

Vincent K Hubbard,
Author: *Swords, Ships, & Sugar: History of Nevis*

"This lovely book is beautifully presented, meticulously researched and a superb example for all historians to follow. Highly recommended!"

Roy Hatley, Editor, www.history.uk.com

"This fascinating story – a true genealogical romance – will enthral those with an interest in history or travel and anyone who has ever conducted any historical family research."

Kevin Gordon, The Sussex Express

"You can feel the effort, care, even love that went into building the island. This connection with the West Indies, and the people who carved their life in a frontier land, is the most romantic tale of all. *Rivers of Time* draws together the streams of several lives."

Definitive Caribbean Guide

"Combining the height of story-telling and intellectual history, two golden threads run through the narrative – scrupulous detective research and intimate contact with the reader. As the author rescues the past from oblivion she reveals the treasures and beauty in the back alleys of history. *Rivers of Time* is not only Nevis's story: it is humanity's story, too."

Dr Kenneth Craven

"To get even a shadowy understanding of men and women in the distant past is exceptionally difficult and is certainly not a task for the faint-hearted; but close attention to recorded actions and the views of their recorders puts at least the outward behaviour of the actors of the day on display."

Frank Barlow,
Preface to *William Rufus* **(Methuen)**

Matador
9 De Montfort Mews
Leicester LE1 7FW , UK
Tel: (+44) 116 255 9311 / 9312
Email: books@troubador.co.uk
Web: www.troubador.co.uk/matador

A Cataloguing-in-Publication (CIP) catalogue record for this book
is available from the British Library.

Typeset in 11pt Centaur Regular
Designed by appliance, Alfriston, UK

Matador is an imprint of Troubador Publishing Ltd

Dedicated to the people of Nevis
and to the memory of
Philippa Prentis Phillips
and
Roland Percival Archibald

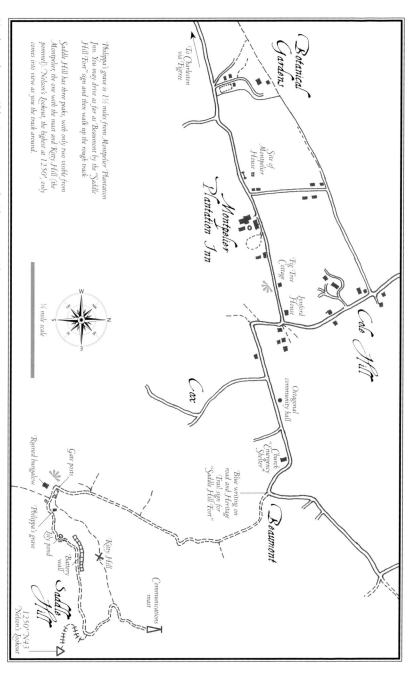

Philippa's grave is 1½ miles from Montpelier Plantation Inn. You may drive as far as 'Beaumont by the "Saddle Hill Fort" sign and then walk up the rough track.

Saddle Hill has three peaks, with only two visible from Montpelier, the one with the mast and Kitty Hill (the pommel). Nelson's Lookout, the highest at 1250', only comes into view as you the track around.

Map showing the route to Philippa's grave from Montpelier Plantation Inn • John Bone

Contents

Illustrations

1 The Tombstone seen from Saddle Hill
2 The Marker Tablet • Lizzie Shepherd
3 The Tombstone • Lizzie Shepherd
4 Nevis Peak from Montpelier • Joan Budd
5 Saddle Hill from Montpelier showing pommel at southern end • Joan Budd
6 17th century pond on Prentis Works where ospreys were seen • Lizzie Shepherd
7 17th century pond showing structure of wall • John Bone
8 Open air shelter built by early settlers • John Guilbert
9 House with wattle walls • John Guilbert
10 17th century cistern • Joan Budd
11 17th century water cooler • Joan Budd
12 The interior of the Hermitage Hotel showing 17th century wooden construction • Joan Budd
13 17th century lime kiln on the Atlantic shore of Nevis • John Guilbert
14 Looking into the lime kiln showing old walls, shells and wood inside • John Guilbert
15 Lime kiln fireplace • John Guilbert
16 18th century sugar mill ruins • John Guilbert
17 Herman Ward at Montpelier • Muffin Hoffman
18 Vince Hubbard with Sandy Claxton • Muffin Hoffman

Preface

This is a true story about an English woman who lived on Nevis in the seventeenth century. In the year following the celebration of the two hundredth anniversary of the Abolition of Slavery, it is not only especially relevant but contains an intriguing and unexpected twist. Only one element is fictional, namely the conversations I believe might have taken place in the seventeenth century. But in all cases the facts stated, together with the speakers and their locations, are based on verifiable historical sources. A list of these will be found at the end of the book.

Two things encouraged me to choose the fictional format for the middle section of the book: first, a letter that Professor Frank Barlow wrote to John Pollock (26.vi.96) in which he wrote: "There are no proofs in history. It's a branch of fiction. There are, however, probabilities"; secondly, because the fictional format provides an opportunity for exercising creative imagination while reconstructing the truly remarkable life of Philippa Prentis Phillips, whose gravestone provided the puzzle.

The order of the chapters reflects the questions I asked and the logic of the investigation but not always the actual sequence in which the research was done and the solutions appeared.

Throughout the centuries the name Prentis is spelt in at least five different ways that range from Prentice to Prenlis to Prentis and beyond! I have therefore used the spelling as it occurs on the gravestone except when quoting directly from historical sources.

The research that has gone into this book is extensive and there was no way that I could have done this single-handedly. Therefore I am deeply grateful for the help given me over nearly twenty years, by friends from many different specialities. I thank: historians, Geraldine Bews, Christine Eickelman, Vince Hubbard, David Small, Peter Webb; the past owners of Montpelier Plantation Inn, James and Celia Milnes-Gaskell, and the present ones, Timothy, Meredith, Lincoln and Muffin Hoffman; genealogist, Diane Hallstrom; archaeologist, Marco Menike; industrial archaeologist, David Rollinson; author, Giles Milton; maritime historian and consultant, Nigel Hunt; geologist-vulcanologist,

Brett Wilson; administrator, Elisabeth Jones; Curator of Maps at the Royal Geographical Society, Francis Herbert; Archivist and Records Manager, Duchy of Cornwall, Elisabeth A. Stuart.

Most especially I must thank Peter Robinson who has now worked with me on four projects as researcher and co-author. His skills are formidable and his discoveries have proved crucial for getting a comprehensive picture of Philippa and her life on Nevis.

I also owe an enormous debt to many Nevisians, most especially to Roland Archibald, whom I met over twenty years ago and his daughter, Judith McGrath, who has been most generous with her time and recollections. Others to whom I am indebted are Herman Ward, stonemason; Averil Richard-Williams, administrator; Hyleta Liburd, teacher and education officer; John Guilbert, Executive Director, Nevis Historical and Conservation Society; Edison Richards, Sandy Claxton, Junior Mills, Miller Pemberton and all the staff at Montpelier.

I must also thank Nick Webb for support and advice; Bill and Lynne Clewes who have helped in innumerable ways; other friends and visitors to Montpelier; the West Country Studies Library, Exeter, for permission to use their pictures; Pam Hewitt for impeccable proof reading; Tony Seddon for the book's layout and jacket design, based on a 18th century print of Nevis; Adam and Siobhan Green, Cate Olson and Nash Robbins for friendship and critical advice. Most of all I am indebted to Cheryl Lutring, who has worked tirelessly on the manuscript with her usual efficiency and skill.

As this book was going to press I learnt that an option on a film had been taken. While this is a most gratifying development, there has been one unexpected consequence. Since a chapter in a book is not a sequence in a film, and a strong screen play demands a deep knowledge of the backcloth to the drama, I have had to re-examine the story from a fresh point of view and, for the first time, come to terms with changes in myself that occurred during the years of my quest. The final chapter, *The Wash of History: A Retrospect*, reflects this.

So, while renewing my gratitude to all those already mentioned, I am delighted to give additional thanks to Pam Barry, Feona Gray, Richard Friedhoff, Justin Hardy, David Jacobs, Simon Lowe, Patrick Miles, Dundas and Sheila Moore, Tony Mulliken, Tina Pepler, Rosemary Matheson, and a host of new friends.

Part One

A wanderer is man from his birth
He was born in a ship
On the breast of the river of Time

§

Matthew Arnold, The Future

Chapter One

Exploring the Present

"For each age is a dream that is dying.
Or one that is coming to birth."

§

Arthur O'Shaughnessy, *Ode*

The Caribbean, one of the most popular tourist destinations in the world, lies half way between the southern tip of Florida and the northern coast of Venezuela. The Tropic of Cancer is nearly five hundred miles to the north, the Equator one thousand miles south. The cool, deep Atlantic Ocean lashes the eastern shores of the islands while warm, shallow Caribbean seas lap the western ones. But even there, in places such as the Cayman Islands, the water can suddenly drop over sheer rocky walls to a depth of three thousand feet.

Some seven thousand tropical islands, islets, reefs and cays make up the land mass, whose crops and wildlife, cultures and dialects are hugely diverse. Large islands such as Grenada, St Lucia, Dominica, and Jamaica, show a whole range of landscapes from humid rainforest on high mountain peaks, to lush plantations and dry sandy shorelines. But most islands, like Bequia and Jost van Dyke, are small. Some are famous for their yachting attractions, such as the Grenadines, or their scary airport approaches, such as Saba, or by the celebrities who have homes there – Mustique and Princess Margaret, Necker and Richard Branson are amongst the best known.

But one small island, Nevis, is famous for a heap of additional reasons that cover British royalty, Lord Nelson, Alexander Hamilton, no casinos, controlled tourism and delightful people. Only thirty-five square miles in area, the island is really an extinct volcano rising to some three thousand feet, whose cone-shaped peak permanently attracts mists. When in 1493, Christopher Columbus first caught sight of this profile he named the island *Nuestro Senora de las Nieves*, Our Lady of the Snows, from which the present name, Nevis, is supposedly derived. In the past the island has also been known as *Dulcina* or *Mavis*.

Driving around the coastal road takes no more than half a day, even while stopping for the odd rum punch. Yet given its minute size Nevis is redolent with history – to a quite remarkable extent. In the late eighteenth century Lord Nelson was one of its most famous visitors. Following the American War of Independence he was stationed there with orders to stop American goods being imported into the islands in exchange for sugar. Given that the trade had already gone on for over a hundred years his was a thankless task. His decisive actions were hugely unpopular with both the Americans and the plantation owners and consequently he was boycotted by local society. But when Prince William, the Captain of HMS Pegasus, turned up everything changed. The Prince – the third son of George III – would leave the Navy in 1789 and forty-one years later become King William IV. The two men became close friends and at Nelson's wedding on 11th March 1787, Prince William gave the bride away. Fanny Nisbett was the niece of John Herbert, the lawyer who had acted for Nelson in his legal battle with the local planters. The ceremony took place at Montpelier House in the south of the island and their marriage certificate can still be seen in the parish church of St John's, Fig Tree.

Two hundred years later another close connection developed with the British royal family, when another Prince William visited. In 1993, Diana, Princess of Wales, recently separated from Prince Charles, brought her young sons for a two-week visit. They stayed at Montpelier Plantation Inn, an elegant hotel built in the grounds of one of the oldest plantations, just up the road from the house where Nelson was married. Princess Diana and her sons were far more popular with the locals than either the previous Prince William or Lord Nelson had ever been and her memory is still poignantly cherished.

Yet despite the unfortunate start, American connections and economic ones, too, remained strong. Alexander Hamilton, one of the Founding Fathers of America, was born on the island – on the wrong side of the blanket, it is claimed. Trading links across the seas were continuous and deep. So vast was Nevis's wealth in the late seventeenth century, that the island was christened *The Queen of the Caribbees*, for its small land mass-produced the best sugar of anywhere in the Caribbean and in the greatest quantity.

I first went to Nevis in January 1985 — not entirely by chance. I had just completed an eighteen-month documentary project which had taken me right around the world, but not, alas, in one go. I had filmed in Bangladesh, then returned to London; then in New York and back to London. Nepal, St Lucia and Montana followed and so it continued. I was exhausted and felt I deserved to indulge. Of all travel writers, I had enjoyed most the articles of Eric Newby, James Morris — as Jan Morris then was — and Mark Ottaway. Mark, the senior travel correspondent of the *Sunday Times*, had written glowingly about Montpelier Plantation Inn: it was his favourite small hotel in the world. So I booked my flights to Nevis without hesitation.

A huge British Airways aeroplane deposited me at Antigua; a minute LIAT one flew me on to Nevis. We stopped first at St Kitts and the next five minutes represented the shortest flight in the world between two countries — all of two miles across the straits. The plane banked sharply over the water and we glided down onto a very short runway. The airport building may have been just an old shed, but Immigration and Customs were very serious affairs indeed. Once outside I had a choice of several very old cars. Weather-beaten Luther, whose age I could not even begin to guess, packed me in with a warm greeting and a warning. Montpelier Plantation Inn was right at the other end of the island. The drive would be long and the light was fading.

We started off south along a small winding road. There were only a few houses, no hotels of any kind that I could see, but donkeys and goats galore. On the left, the tree-covered slopes of the mountain poured down to the shoreline. On the right, a superb, vast plantation of coconut palm stretched inland along the whole length of a seven-mile beach. This, Luther told me, was called Pinney's Beach after an early English settler who arrived as a 'criminal' and died a millionaire. We ambled through the main street of Charlestown, the sleepy, dusty and run-down capital, then Luther turned east. For nearly four miles we climbed up a road where the ratio of pot holes to tarmac was at least fifty-fifty and as we rose, the views of Nevis Peak increasingly dominated. Suddenly, on the right hand side, I saw a beaten up rum shop and here Luther turned along a dirt road. We bounced down a hill, up a hill, then down another, even more wriggly and steep. We steered through potholes, over boulders and deep muddy ruts, into the back of beyond. Then finally the car puffed its way through two iron gates into a courtyard. On the left was a simple plantation house with characteristic first floor balconies. Across the courtyard was an exquisite, large ancient hall guarded by an enormous ficus tree, while away to the left was the original mill tower of this old sugar plantation.

By the time I finally arrived I was deeply in love with Nevis and have returned there regularly ever since. Over the years, Nevis and its citizens, Montpelier Plantation Inn and its owners and visitors have given me so much – respite from work, fascinating experiences, the chance to know a variety of people of many nationalities and occupations, ranging from well known writers to the first woman captain of a New England fishing boat who survived the monster waves featured in the story *The Perfect Storm*. True, I missed Princess Diana and her sons by just two weeks, but I did meet a film star so famous and handsome that when I truthfully told my nieces he had taken me out to dinner, they reacted first with total disbelief and then deep envy.

But above all, Nevis provided me with a puzzle that has obsessed me for over twenty years. Between projects that have kept me busy and the passing years that have made me older, this mystery has kept me beavering away. Finally, I think I may have solved it. The challenge first presented itself on the second morning of my very first stay.

Chapter Two

Touching the Past

"No nation was ever ruined by trade."

§

Benjamin Franklin, *Essays: Thoughts On Commercial Subjects*

The accommodation at Montpelier is in small cottages dotted around the garden. Simple and beautifully furnished they had no air conditioning – though they do now. So before going to sleep that first night, I opened the curtains and let the Trade Winds blow right through the room and woke with the first rays of the rising sun.

Owned by James and Celia Milnes-Gaskell, an English couple who had already been on the island for fifteen years, the hotel featured welcome touches of English luxury, like real tea leaves and a proper tea-pot. Better still, a single professional woman travelling alone was not placed at the smallest table near the service doors of the dining room, but treated superbly – welcomed, introduced to people, drawn into all events whenever I wished. Immediately I felt part of a most agreeable family party. Though the conversion from a ruined plantation to a luxury hotel had taken place not many years before, the grounds were already a green panoply of lawns, palms and ferns. In the small flower bed beneath my terrace, humming birds flitted amongst the blossoms; small, cheeky, black finches with bright orange breasts chased canary-coloured ones, each aggressively defending their territories.

I had taken my tea onto the terrace and as I drank looked south eastward towards the twin peaks of Saddle Hill, the western one rising up like a pommel. The view was inviting, the air delicious. England's winter with its grey fogs, cold temperatures and short dark days was thousands of miles away. I decided to walk to the ridge on the skyline.

Relishing being able to wear just cotton slacks and a short-sleeved shirt, I set off at a brisk pace – through the car park, then right down a lane that would be a mud bath in the wet, summer season. Breasting a small slope, I waved to a braying donkey on the left and walked on for a further two hundred yards. At the T-junction I turned right, then almost immediately left and on through the valley to Cox Village. Cocks and hens scattered across the path; goats and kids scurried off the verges into the bush. The rural bustle of a West Indian day was taking over, the sound of water being drawn against a counterpoint of chattering children getting ready for school.

At the end of the village I began to climb around the side of a steep hill. After half a mile I took a rough track through thick scrubland – the only way up to the ridge. Land crabs scuttled sideways in the mud; a group of chattering monkeys, suddenly spotting me, shot across my path in startled bounds.

The walk was exhilarating and the rise of the sun kept pace with the rise of the hill. Some fifteen minutes later, when I was nearing the lower ridge, I saw two heavy stone columns forming pillars for entrance gates to the land beyond. But oddly, there were no gates.

I passed between the pillars onto a level piece of grass and stopped to catch my breath. Directly below me the slope of Saddle Hill fell to the plain and the sea beyond. To the north-west I could see the island of St Kitts very clearly. Beyond lay the stark outline of Saint Eustatius and some forty miles away, the faint silhouette of Saba.

I turned back east towards Saddle Hill, along a path running between a big cistern on the left and a modern house on my right. As I passed, a man appeared in the doorway and waved in greeting.

"Good morning, ma'am," he said.

"Good morning," I replied. "What a lovely day."

As he came towards me, I saw a slim Nevisian, about five feet ten inches who carried himself very erect. The lines on his face and the wear of his hands suggested someone who worked the land. I guessed he was in his early seventies.

"You've come up from Montpelier?" This was more a statement than a query.

"Yes, I have. The day was too good to waste."

"And you live in England, ma'am?"

"Yes."

"I have family members in Leeds, Birmingham and Sheffield. You must be hot from the climb. Would you like some water?"

"Thank you very much."

"Then please come in."

He led the way to the front of his house. But though the door was open, he took me onto a terrace at the side, where the full glory of the view was revealed. There he left me, disappeared into the house and shortly returned with a glass of cold water.

"Have you lived here long?" I asked.

"Long on Nevis but not long at this house. I am an *estater*."

I had never heard that word before and I must have looked puzzled for he explained, "I have estates."

"So all this land is yours?"

His smile combined great sweetness and pride.

"Well, yes. But there's still a lot of work to be done up here, for it's badly overgrown. Not like in the early years."

How long ago were those early years, I wondered, and what were they like.

As I finished the water, he said, "My name is Roland Archibald."

"And mine is June Goodfield."

"I am pleased to meet you, ma'am. I'd like to show you something special. Will you come walk with me?"

I had no hesitation in following this gentle man. He led the way back to the footpath and turned east. The path was very rough, full of volcanic stone and covered with thorn bushes that scratched at my slacks. Still he kept on, walking rapidly. Then at the slope's edge, he stopped and pointed south-east across the sea.

"There is Montserrat. The small island in front is Redondo. On a clear day you can see as far as Guadaloupe."

But there was haze over the sea and only Montserrat and rocky Redondo stood out, illuminated by rays of sunlight.

Now Roland Archibald turned away and walked straight towards the bulk of Saddle Hill. But after another twenty yards he suddenly veered left into dense bush. This time my skin was scratched right through my slacks. Pushing aside the shrubs, he led the way to a minute clearing and there I saw a tombstone.

"Read what it says," he invited.

As I approached the waist-high structure something immediately struck me as incongruous. The supporting stones and masonry seemed identical with those of the cistern I had seen near his house. Yet the slab on top was totally different – old and broken in half, with the two diagonal pieces roughly repaired with modern cement.

I lent over the tomb. The words were easy to read since the sunlight cast a deep shadow and the letters stood out clearly.

"Read what it says," he repeated.

I traced the words with my forefinger and spoke them out aloud.

Here lyeth the body
of Philippa Prentis
Phillips, the wife of
Clement Prentis and
after his decease
the wife of William Phillips
Departed her Life August the XI,
Anno Domini 1683.

I suddenly found myself very moved, looking at a gravestone commemorating the life of a woman who surely must have been one of the earliest settlers on the island. Eager to ask questions, I glanced back at Roland Archibald but something in his expression stopped me. He was still gazing intently at the tablet.

I believe an entire minute went by before he spoke again.

"She loved it up here. I come up every day to talk to her and when I die, I am going to be buried here too."

Once again I was deeply moved. But I was also utterly astonished. Why did he say that? How could he know what she had loved? I smiled at him invitingly, but he said nothing more and I did not want to pry. So in silence we walked back to the house.

Racing back down the two miles to the hotel, the questions piled up in my mind. Who was Philippa? Where did she live before coming to Nevis? When did she arrive? Why did she come? Did she have children by either of her two husbands? Were any of her descendants on the island; were they anywhere in fact? Most puzzling of all, just why did a quiet, dignified Nevisian *estater*, living three hundred years later, want to be buried in an isolated spot next to a woman he could never have known – one who might well have owned his ancestors as slaves?

§

Whether lying in bed, with the familiar trade winds providing a night-time lullaby, or walking the seven-mile Pinney Beach – positively virginal in those days, with not a single hotel to be seen – my thoughts constantly returned to Philippa. I yearned to know more about her, to understand her life, interpret her world of centuries ago. Yet at the same time I was puzzled why this person, intrigued me so much. The mystery was certainly challenging but there was something else. For some reason I already felt a deep identification with her. I had recently gone through a painful period in my life – a miscarriage, divorce and my brother's death all in just a few short months. Philippa would have to be strong, would have had to struggle against enormous odds. I doubted that had I lived in her times, I could have even survived in a strange country, let alone succeeded.

But even using the word 'succeeded' was sheer speculation. I didn't know the first thing about Philippa, except that her ancient tablet lay on what seemed to me to be a modern tombstone. Yet her mystery – evoked by a gravestone carrying just three facts and the emotional words of a living Nevisian – formed an irresistible challenge. Since my documentary project was complete, I had time on my hands and anticipated that resolving her puzzle would be very straightforward. A systematic and careful study of the records – tracing genealogies, examining land deeds, unearthing wills, interpreting edicts – should rapidly reveal the story of Philippa on Saddle Hill and why Roland Archibald said what he had said.

Chapter Three

Recovering the Records

"The past is the only dead thing that smells sweet."

§

Edward Thomas, *Early One Morning.*

I remember the next day equally vividly for my optimism was quickly dashed. During the night the Christmas winds returned in force — a welcome sign that the humid hurricane season was over. But the winds could still trigger torrential showers and all that night I heard incessant drumming as the clouds burst over Nevis. Even the donkey was silent.

In the morning the mists were not only down on Nevis Peak, but blanketing Saddle Hill as well. Contemplating the walk from my cottage to the breakfast courtyard with a towel round my neck and sheltering under a huge umbrella, I knew it was simply a question of deciding which lake to walk through.

However, it was a perfect day to search for Philippa in the archives and I was advised to visit the Alexander Hamilton Museum in Charlestown. Luther picked me up and once again we bounced along the two concrete parallel tracks leading to the main road. Progress was at a stately five miles an hour, and even though the horn sounded often, stops were frequent as we waited behind mini taxi after mini taxi, whose names ranged from the deeply religious — *Praise the Lord, Charity* — to the totally secular — *Red Rat, Renegade.*

Once on the main road, the journey was somewhat faster, but not much. I asked Luther to take me via the Garden of Eden, the site of famous bath springs that most early settlers and sailors had used and many Nevisians still do. The name is apt, the situation sylvan, and innocence still often present!

The hot water comes from deep within the volcano of Nevis Peak and emerges hundreds of feet further down, about a mile outside Charlestown. The faint smell of sulphur and the intense heat led the sailors to ascribe miraculous curative powers to the waters, but a good hot wash after a long, filthy sea voyage was just as effective as any miracle.

But this was no day for bathing, so we went straight on to the Hamilton Museum, set in a small, grassed area in the northern section of Charlestown, about one hundred yards beyond the jetty. There is no harbour.

I planned to study the Court Records because I was confident I would find Philippa and her husbands there. For whether in the West Indies or America, one of the first things the earliest settlers established was a Court House, with proper accounts of births, marriages, wills, deaths and land ownership. Later church records would be an important source, but in the very earliest years there were no churches for unlike the Spaniards, the English settlers didn't take a priest along.

The curator was most welcoming and asked how she could help. As she led me across the room I told her that I would like to see the Court Records from about 1650 to 1685. She stopped dead in her tracks and gave me a rueful smile.

"You are not the first person who'd love to see them, but I regret we cannot show them to you."

I gazed at her with astonishment and again she smiled ruefully.

"... because you see, when the French invaded Nevis in 1706, the first thing they did was to go to the Court House, pull out all the records and publicly burn them in a great bonfire. Then they burned down the building as well."

"Trying to pretend the English had never been here?"

"Exactly. May I ask your particular interest?"

"Well, yesterday I walked up Saddle Hill and was shown the tombstone of Philippa Prentis Phillips. I'd love to know who she was and where she came from."

The curator laughed. "Again you are not the first! We'd all love to know. She is one of our oldest mysteries. But our seventeenth century records are sparse in the extreme. Still we have a few documents and books which might be helpful."

She produced some four photocopied pages – notes from a book that, she said, recorded some of the first settlers in the Americas between 1654 and 1685. Since the pattern of the winds dictated that ships sailing from England had to come via the Caribbean, St Christopher – as St Kitts was then called – and Nevis were regular ports of call, both for replenishing water and supplies and dropping off those who were staying on the islands. But though my scanning produced the names of a few people, there was no one called Philippa, nor Clement Prentis nor William Phillips.

After spending about half an hour making notes, I knew I was at a dead end and recalling my supreme confidence of the previous day it was my turn to be rueful. There was no chance that copies had ever been made of the Nevis Court Records, let alone miraculously preserved in England and I had only the stone with the names of one woman, two husbands and a date of death. But no maiden name, no birth date, no age at which Philippa died.

Nevertheless, I felt I had to go back to the tomb and on my next visit, I did.

Chapter Four

Secrets in Stone

"The land was ours before we were the land's."

§

Robert Frost, *The Gift Outright.*

By then I had become friends with David Rollinson, who, with his wife, had lived on Nevis for over forty years. A Canadian engineer and specialist on the sugar mill industry, we had often discussed Philippa and the puzzle she presented. So I was delighted when one day he suggested we go up to the tomb with Brett Wilson, a geologist and vulcanologist from Yorkshire, who had once been a school teacher on Nevis. We drove up in David's Jeep, parked near Roland Archibald's house, which by now was ruined and deserted, and walked to the tomb.

David, short, stout and relaxed, was in his late fifties and wore spectacles. Brett, about forty-five, thin and lanky, with long hair was far more intense. He went straight to the tablet and patted it affectionately.

"When I lived on Nevis," he volunteered, speaking in a soft, gentle voice, "I came up pretty much every day and talked to Philippa regularly. She knows more about me than anyone. I wanted to live here, but both my previous girlfriend and my present wife said Nevis was too small. So I told her all about my problems."

"Had you stayed, I am sure she would have looked after you!" I said.

"I am sure she would. But let's start," he went on briskly. "I gather you want to know whether her tablet was made on or off the island?"

"That's the idea," said David. "We know some people used to order their tombstones from England already carved — with just a space left for the date of death. But since these were mostly made of marble, that was an expensive option, even though the stone was used as ballast on the voyage."

"Okay," said Brett briskly, "let's first try to establish whether or not the tablet actually is Nevis stone. Take a look at the Saddle Hill rocks all around here and take one fact on board. Though Saddle Hill now has two peaks, each is made of different volcanic material. The eastern peak has much darker stones than the western peak. Yet both came out in the same eruption."

"How could that be?" I asked.

"Because the exploding magma chamber had two layers. A light-coloured layer erupted first, then a darker layer came out and landed on top of it."

Brett picked up a stone and handed it to me. "Look, you can see the result here – dark pieces set in a matrix of whitish crystals. But in Philippa's slab there are no whitish crystals typical of a Saddle Hill eruption, nor solely black ones that are typical of Nevis Peak. This is our first clue."

"So the stone for her tablet didn't come from either place?"

"No. Nevertheless from what I can see I believe her tablet was made on the island - and we can work out precisely where. You have to realise that aeons ago, Nevis had some ten active volcanoes. Eruptions began in the north of the island. Hurricane Hill blew next. That's to the west of the airport and will be bulldozed if the runway is extended – which God forbid it ever will. After that the volcanic activity moved south to Saddle Hill – which had four, smaller erupting peaks. And finally, Mount Nevis in the centre, blew last of all ... and boy, did it ever!"

"Exciting times," I observed.

Brett was grinning. "Very. But the excitement was spread over at least two million years. Now take a real close look at the tablet. Can you see any whitish crystals or any black ones in the stone?"

I peered carefully, then shook my head.

"Nor can I. This means not only must we rule out Saddle Hill and Nevis Peak, but Butler's Mountain as well. Let me come clean. The geology of the stone tells me that Philippa's tablet came from eruptions at either Cade's Bay or Hurricane Hill. Both are near the site of old Jamestown. When she died this was the capital of Nevis and the centre of trade, and this is where someone carving gravestones would be based"

"Yet even though the tablet was carved down at Jamestown, Philippa could still have been buried up here."

"Oh, absolutely," replied Brett emphatically, "I'm not suggesting for a moment that she wasn't. You take the tablet to the grave. But, I repeat, it would be made wherever somebody was carving stone."

I looked at the tablet again. "What's this hole in the top?" I asked.

"I don't really know," replied Brett. David, too, shook his head. "Maybe there was some decoration of some kind, that's fallen out."

"But what about the stones of the tomb?" I asked, "They look identical to those of the cistern by the house."

"We'll examine the cistern in a minute. But for the moment look carefully at the stones used to build the tomb."

As I moved even closer David stopped me.

"Get to the other side," he warned. "You are about to step on a large ants' nest!"

I moved very quickly as Brett continued.

"You'll see that there are only black crystals in them, and this tells us that all these stones came from the very last Nevis Peak eruption. Geologically, they are totally different from the stone of Philippa's tablet. And it's obvious that the cement holding them together is also the same cement that was used to repair the break across the tablet."

"But if this is an old tablet on a modern tombstone, do you think Philippa is actually in here?"

"Not for one moment." Both men were emphatic, but I was astonished.

I began tapping the tomb as a doctor taps a chest. David repeated my actions using a small screwdriver. The sides sounded dense, but when we tapped the tablet the sound from below was clearly hollow.

Now David reached into his bag and retrieved a small, thin tube and a hammer. He knelt down at the west end of the tomb and gently tapped the tube underneath the plinth.

"I can't get this in at all. It's solid rock. All the land here is solid rock. You couldn't bury a body here without a hell of a lot of clearing and hard digging. I'm quite certain Philippa lies in land somewhere below the house."

He turned to face me directly. "You must appreciate that people on Nevis were quite used to burying their relatives in their gardens. They placed them just three feet deep in a shallow grave, aligned east-west — as is Philippa's tomb. Even though there are churchyards now, sometimes they still bury people on their land because the garden is often the only space available. This happens in other Caribbean islands, too. I've seen graves in yards and gardens in Tortola and Anguilla and Montserrat."

"So Roland Archibald did not take me to a grave?"

"No," said David, "just to a memorial. Believe me, had Roland Archibald found Philippa's skeleton, he would have left it undisturbed. Nevisians are most respectful of the dead and where they lie. In fact, most are downright nervous. If they get too close the dead '*jumbies*' will return to haunt them."

Once again I was singularly moved. We walked back to the Jeep in silence, but some twenty yards before the house, David stopped. To our left we could just make out a rough track dropping steeply to the valley below. At its edge was a pond lined with large stone walls and filled with reeds and water lilies.

"This is one of the very earliest ponds on the island – seventeenth-century," said David. "There's another one – exactly the same – on land just above Philippa's tomb. The construction is quite superb. There's no masonry holding those rounded stones together, yet even after all this time they fit so closely that the pond still holds water." He paused and looked down the track. "I just want to take a look down here. I'll join you in a few minutes."

He moved off and I heard his shoes scuffing at the earth. Brett led me straight to the cistern and leant on its edge.

"As you guessed, these stones are the same as those on the tomb, rectangular and smooth. Somebody put real work into dressing them. And see those black tabular crystals again. They also came from Nevis Peak."

"But I don't understand," I objected. "Roland Archibald was surrounded by tons of stone up here. So why go somewhere else to get different ones for the cistern and the tomb? It would be an enormous job to haul them all up here."

"Ah! You are forgetting something. Since the stones needed to be shaped and dressed they would come from wherever people were quarrying and they weren't doing that on Saddle Hill. Actually they didn't come from all that far away. The Methodist church in Gingerland, just over on the Atlantic side of Saddle Hill, is made from the same Nevis Peak rock."

He hesitated and peered over the edge of the cistern's walls. "It's most unlikely that when Roland Archibald finished building his cistern, there just happened to be enough stones left over for a tomb. It is far too much of a coincidence. David and I both think he built it deliberately."

"But why? And where did he find the tablet then?" I asked.

"We may never know the answer to either of those questions. He died in 1990."

"I'd like to go back on to the terrace where he first took me," I said.

"I'd like to come with you. Haven't seen the place for years. I'd only been on the island three weeks when Hurricane Hugo struck. I remember coming up here and seeing the ruined house. The roof had gone and the walls were badly damaged, but the furniture was still in place around the television set. It was very, very spooky.

"Afterwards, I walked up towards Saddle Hill and so met Philippa for the first time. Then on the way up I found the other ancient pond that David mentioned. An osprey was fishing there. I was amazed. I didn't even know they came so high up into this neck of the woods and I wondered if it was her free spirit returning."

Brett was a very gentle and spiritual man and the back of my neck was tingling.

We trod gingerly round the ruin, carefully avoiding the glass shards on the floor. From the balcony the view across the plain to the sea was as spectacular as ever. By then David had joined us again and his hands were full. We crowded round.

"That's the stem of a clay pipe which we'll be able to date from the diameter of the bore. Then there's some slate from Wales, from a much later date. But the bit I really like is this."

He put a small piece of pottery into my hand.

"I think it's part of a Bellarmine jug from the 1660s. We'll check this. But that's the only pottery I've ever seen with a similar brown glaze."

"Just what are the implications of all this?" I asked.

"Put together everything we've seen today and the evidence leads to only one conclusion. Generations ago people were living and working up here." Now Brett left the balcony and scrambled down through scrub so thick that soon we couldn't see him at all. But we heard his yell all right.

"There's a really old wall down here – running at right angles to the path. It's made of the Saddle Hill stone – the same as the walls of the ponds."

David now turned back to me and though he spoke quietly I could sense his excitement. "This is your starting point. I've always thought that somewhere around here was the settlement where Philippa lived. I think with a little clearing and excavation we could establish this. If we studied under magnification, the black and white aerial survey photographs that were taken in 1946, I bet we could see the line of the old walls and this would tell us where to start digging."

Chapter Five

Seeking New Worlds

'Imagine a closet without enough headroom for standing up straight,
packed with boxes, bales, rope, hammocks and assorted gear, fill the spaces in between
with people who haven't been able to take a bath for weeks, and who have been suffering,
tossing and turning, in heavy seas. Make the atmosphere damp and cold; put the
fear of the unknown in the minds of the occupants, and this will give a
mild approximation of what it was like to be aboard.'

§

A Goodly Ship: The Building of the Susan Constant,
Peter H. Spectre & David Larkin, 1992

So by now I had garnered three more significant facts. Philippa's marker tablet
had been made on Nevis; she wasn't inside the tomb; there had been a settlement
in the lee of Saddle Hill. But what else did these facts reveal? Not very much
at all actually. What might I justifiably conclude? Again, very little with any
certainty but some things with caution. First of all, Philippa clearly wasn't
from a wealthy family whose confident head had marker tablets inscribed
before sailing from England. Even if he had, it was unlikely that his wife – if
she was his wife – had accompanied him, for records show this was an
exceedingly rare event. In any case one would expect the wife's name on the
husband's tablet, not the husband's on the wife's – as they were on Philippa's.

Secondly, whoever Philippa's two husbands were, they were clearly not
dirt poor. Because then her grave would have been marked by a simple wooden
cross that would have disintegrated within a decade or so, as rain, tropical
storms and hurricanes wreaked havoc. Thirdly, since she had married twice, it
was likely – though not impossible – that she wasn't a teenager when she died,
though it was possible that she was in her twenties.

Finally the fact that there was a memorial commemorating her life alone, in the form of a marker tablet which had clearly cost real money, suggested that she was likely a mature woman and a respected member of her family. For at a time when life expectancies were short and wresting a living from the land difficult, such expenditure was never lightly undertaken. On the other hand, the decade in which she died was a time when Nevis was at the height of its wealth, so possibly her family, along with many others, were doing really well from sugar cane.

However, the fact that Philippa was *not* in the tomb shed no light whatsoever on who she was. Had a skeleton been inside I would have sought permission to open up the tomb and take some small bone samples. If tested in an appropriate laboratory it might have been possible to determine whether she was an adolescent, or a child-bearing adult, or post-menopausal and osteoporotic. From the secrets of the bone I could have deduced an age within at least a range of ten years. Having determined that I could have worked back to a possible date of birth, and so a possible time when she might have arrived in Nevis and an historical period in which to start searching the records.

But the only facts I had were linked to an end of a life. I needed to investigate its beginning. One way to start was to study what was happening in England in the second and third quarters of the seventeenth century, and find out why people were coming to the Caribbean and if any records of them and their voyages existed. My attention would now have to switch from Nevis and study documents thousands of miles away in England, but I hadn't a clue where to start.

However, Brett and David referred me to David Watts' book on the West Indies and told me to focus on the chapter, *Early Northwest European Plantations*. So I studied this carefully. Watts pointed out that the activities of pirates and privateers preceded legal trade and the establishment of permanent colonies. The initial penetration of European nations into the Caribbean had its origins in attempts to break the trading monopoly of Spain, by attacking the Spanish treasure fleets. To begin with most *corsairs* were French, but after 1540 they were increasingly joined by the English. In all cases the raids were mostly conducted with connivance of their home governments, though their support was sometimes indirect and always denied!

One of the most famous of the privateers was William Hawkins, who came from a distinguished Plymouth family. Though in the 1530s, during the reign of Henry VIII, he was engaged in legal trade with Brazil, by the 1540s he had moved into more dubious activities. His son John, later to be knighted, moved to the Court in London where his proposed expeditions also attracted much financial support. Fitting out these ships required money and the financial backers came from those who supported business interests in Dieppe, London and Plymouth. Plymouth provided the commanders, the sailors, the ships, the technical expertise and the management of the enterprises, while London provided the weaponry, the powder and the cash.

However, as the sixteenth century progressed privateering gradually came to coexist alongside a series of trading agreements, which though more or less formal, were in fact technically illicit. That they could be carried on at all was due mostly to the transportation of slaves from West Africa to the northern coasts of the Spanish territories. The slaves were exchanged for dyes, hides, ginger, which fetched high prices in Europe. But all this took place well away from the gaze of government officials.

So the pattern of maritime activity see-sawed between privateering and trade. In 1562, John Hawkins undertook the first major trading voyage of this type. His second voyage concentrated on the Spanish Main. His third expedition to the same territory provoked a furious Spanish response and most of Hawkins' fleet was destroyed, though his nephew, the young Francis Drake, one of his commanders, survived. Seventeen years later Drake sacked the Spanish-occupied town of Santa Domingo and this success, too, provoked even more piracy at the expense of commerce.

Yet the ultimate outcome of these conflicts was stalemate. Though during the last years of Queen Elizabeth's reign, Spain claimed all the territories in the West Indies, increasingly they found they had neither money, manpower nor shipping to defend them. France and England were equally frustrated, for they had neither broken the overall Spanish trade monopoly nor established permanent bases in the West Indies. So by 1604, when James I had been on the English throne for one year, a sort of truce emerged: Spanish monopolies were recognised in lands already occupied by Spain, but there was no such recognition in territories they did not occupy. Finally in 1609, The Treaty of Antwerp paved the way for permanent settlement in the West Indies by people from other European nations.

This is precisely what took place and on a large scale. Between 1620 and 1642, eighty thousand men – nearly two percent of the total male population of England – left to settle abroad. Fifty eight thousand went to North America and the West Indies. Some contemporary writers were puzzled since the English were regarded as staid stay-at-homes. One referred to them as being *'wedded to their native soils like a snaile to its shell, but they'd rather even starve at home than seek stoare abroade'*. Starving at home they certainly were. Though the constraints of the feudal system were gradually eroding, life for the bulk of the population was appallingly hard, trapped as they were in a web of poverty, malnutrition and illness. Only the few wealthiest families lived well. For most, houses were small, cold and damp; fuel scarce, diet restricted and starvation frequent. As Watts showed, communication between settlements was so difficult that villages had to be self-supporting and if the crops failed there was no ready alternative source of food. Moreover, crop failure could be national as well as local, as happened between 1630 and 1633, when a mini ice age set in. Even after the harvest the barns at Nottingham were empty and huge numbers of beggars were crowding the streets of York.

Bad though the situation was, it still might not have been enough to propel people across the oceans. But now persuasion was added to starvation. Companies that had invested in the new colonies had a direct financial interest in their success, and their persuasive propaganda shows that spin is not exclusive to twenty-first century political policy. Several arguments were promulgated: over-crowding was the root cause of everyone's troubles; immense personal fortunes were available for the taking in empty lands across the seas. Since large numbers of the population could now actually read and write, the message acted a genuine stimulus, no matter that it was both oversimplified and over-optimistic.

But most importantly, one further factor emerged which remains totally unexplained to this day. During the first half of the seventeenth century, male births doubled in relation to female births and surplus, unmarried men formed a core group willing to try life overseas. But as was quickly realised, establishing a colony on a permanent basis not only depended on farmers, labourers and craftsmen, beside warriors, sailors and privateers, but women too. Without women there would be no children; without children there would be no future generations to inherit and develop the land.

This in brief is the background against which we must consider the story of Philippa and Nevis. The island was settled around 1628 and in *The True Travels of Captaine Smith* we have a first hand account.

*The last yeare, 1628, Master Littleton, with some others got
a patent of the Earle of Carlisle to plant the isle called the
Barbados, thirty leagues northwards of St Christophers ... but
when they came there, they found it such a baron rocke they lefte
it, although they were told as much before they would not believe
it, persuading themselves ...*

*At last because they would be absolute, they came to Nevis, a
little ile beside St Christopher's where they settled themselves well
furnished with all necessities, being about the number of 100,
and since increased to 150 persons, many were old planters of St
Christophers especially Anthony Hinton and Edward Tenson.
But because all these iles for the most part are so capable to
produce, and in nature so like each other, let this discourse serve
for a description of their all ...*

In the extracts from the St Christopher entry is the first mention of women.

*The 18th March 1624 arrived Captaine Jefferson with
3 men passengers in the Hopewell of London, with some trade
for the Indians, then we had another crop of tobacco ... with
this crop Captaine Warner returned for England in September
1625.*

*Thus we continued til neere June that the Tortels came
in, 1627, but the French being liked to star, sought to
suppose [suppress] us, and all the Cassado, Potatoes and
Tobacco we had planted, but we did prevent them.*

The 26th October came in Captaine William Smith in the
Hopewell with some ordinance, shot and powder, from the Earl
of Carlisle, with Captaine Pelham and 30 men, about that time
also came the Plow; also a small ship of Bristow [Bristol] with
Captaine Warner's wife and 6 or 7 women more.

All this I read but just exactly where in England should I start looking?

§

I was pointed in the crucial direction by a retired Master Mariner, who specialised in maritime and commercial history. One year I decided to follow Philippa's route and cross the Atlantic on a cruise liner leaving her summer station in the Mediterranean to relocate in the Caribbean for the winter. The ship would leave Southampton in mid November and I would disembark in St Kitts some ten days later. Late autumn is not a time for gentle sea breezes and accommodating swells. In my earlier years following four operations on an ear I had been prone to sea sickness so I worried about how well I would cope.

I need not have worried at all. In what everyone agreed was the most unbelievable meteorological conditions, the sea, whether in the Channel, the Bay of Biscay or the Mid Atlantic, was as smooth as a billiard table the entire way. By far the roughest part of the trip was on the small boat taking me across from St Kitts to Nevis, where I was bounced around and got completely soaked though wasn't in fact sick.

But the voyage was memorable for other reasons. First of all, it seemed that the entire cast of *The Calendar Girls* was sailing, for the ship was packed with a slew of Yorkshire people revelling in the calm seas and sun. The second was the standard of hygiene on board, one so excellent that many of us felt the UK Ministry of Health should invite P&O to tackle the problem of the MRSA infection in hospitals. Wiping hands was mandatory as one entered a restaurant, or even passed the buffet section on deck. Charming Indian stewards stood at the entrance and no one could enter until they had received a shot of alcohol, not down the throat, but on the hands.

But from my point of view the third blessing was the presence on board of Nigel Hunt who was giving a series of comprehensive lectures on the history of maritime affairs in the Caribbean. These were beautifully illustrated, excellently delivered and I had no hesitation in asking if he would meet me for a drink so I could lay before him the problem of Philippa.

As a Master Mariner, Nigel had sailed the seven seas for over twenty-five years. He had weathered storm and tempest, an attack by pirates, his ship breaking apart and drifting in the Pacific and worst of all, endless negotiations with bureaucrats on politico-commercial matters. Yet to look at him you would think that nothing stressful had come his way.

Though a short man he exuded a quiet, professional assurance that stemmed from simple traits. He rarely spoke until he was certain of his facts; when he acted he did so with decisiveness. After he had retired, he set up a marine consultancy and as a personal sideline, had specialised in maritime commercial history. From time to time he was also called upon to investigate piracy and fraudulent insurance claims. He was kept very busy indeed.

I briefed him about Philippa and mentioned how in 1706 the French had made a great bonfire of the Nevis Court Records. Though I had no idea where she might have come from, where in the records might be the best place to start my search? I had read David Watt's book; I had been told to examine the City Court books of Bristol, but should I perhaps be looking at Plymouth – where I knew the Pilgrim Fathers had sailed from?

Nigel's answer was definitive: "I wouldn't totally rule out any other ports, but Bristol is definitely your best starting point and there's a very good reason why."

"Why?" I prompted.

"How long have you got? It's all to do with commerce. During the fourteenth and fifteenth centuries, England ran a highly sophisticated overseas trading network. Wine for wool; spices for metal – you know the kind of thing. Trade was excellent. But the Reformation changed everything. Catholic merchants were not allowed to trade with Protestant countries and Protestant merchants couldn't trade in Catholic countries. Of course there were those who broke sanctions, but generally our overseas trade was lost.

"However around the turn of the seventeenth century – post Treaty of Antwerp and all that – when the religious tensions subsided somewhat, commerce rapidly picked up again and an interesting thing happened. A marked monopoly developed in the English regions. Newcastle was allowed to trade to the north – which essentially meant Scandinavia. London's area was to the east – the Lowlands, the Pas de Calais and that part of northern France. Southampton took the south – right down the coastline of Biscay to northern Spain and the northern Mediterranean.

"But Bristol really took the plum for it had the west. Its trading regions not only included Iceland and Ireland, but Portugal, Madeira and the Canaries. I reckon that ninety percent of everything – but everything – leaving England and heading west, passed through Bristol. The city's trade was enormous. Moreover, Bristol's merchants were in a unique position because the sailors manning their ships regularly met the Portuguese and so learned of the mystical, wealthy golden lands far away to the west and this provided another imperative. So that's why I'd start with Bristol."

"If I do find Philippa and the ship she sailed on, what would the conditions have been like?"

"Diabolical – cramped, smelly, overcrowded. Forget the eight hours it takes to fly the Atlantic or the ten days we'll take to get to St Kitts. If the weather was bad they could have taken over three months."

"… because of the pattern of the winds?"

"But of course. They'd have to beat out of the Channel. If they were very lucky they might reach across Biscay, but would most likely face south-westerly gales head on. Once across the Iberian Sea and past Madeira and the Canaries, they'd seek the Trade Winds and set course south-west, hoping to make landfall somewhere in the West Indies. If it was winter and they were going on up to Virginia, then you'd need to add at least another month.

"And remember the size of their ships. Ellen MacArthur went solo around the world in a seventy-five foot trimaran. In those days, seventy-five feet was big – big. The *Susan Constant* – one of the ships that first sailed to Jamestown – was just fifty feet. There was hardly enough room to turn around, yet she carried seventy-one men who had to take turns to lie down and sleep."

"They would have been very happy to arrive."

"If they were still alive, they'd have been very happy," Nigel said laconically.

After ten tranquil and utterly calm days the ship tied up alongside the pier at St Kitts. Being the only person to disembark I was summoned to the dining room where Customs & Immigration quizzed me about why I wished to stay so long. I was given a one month permit and told that I would have to renew this with the immigration authorities on Nevis – an encounter that turned out to be very profitable.

Chapter Six
Change Beyond Belief

'Change is not made without inconvenience, even from worse to better.'

§

Richard Hooker, quoted by Samuel Johnson in the Preface to *The English Dictionary*

The island had changed greatly: the Four Seasons Hotel now occupied a vast site on Pinney's Beach; just inland the magnificent coconut plantation had metamorphosed into a golf course; the ratio of potholes to tarmac on the roads had increased greatly in favour of the tarmac; though Hurricane Hill still stood, the airport runway had been extended and the Arrivals building was no longer a shed, though not yet the modern, typical airport structure that it would later become. Whereas in 1985 many people were riding donkeys, now most were driving their own cars, yet animals still scurried across all the roads. But now the donkeys that cars had replaced, trotted everywhere, sometimes disappearing into the bush only to reappear on the tarmac a bit further on. Their herds were flourishing, so agonised and passionate discussions were taking place as to how to control the numbers. The mango trees were in splendid shape and so too were the monkeys, who had the irritating habit of picking the ripe fruit, taking one bite, then discarding the rest.

The path up to Saddle Hill was a deserted as ever and actually even rougher; Roland Archibald's house was even more of a decaying ruin, though the views were just as superb. The scrub around Philippa's tomb had been cleared, though if you didn't know where to look, it was not easy to spot – even though it was a mere ten yards from the main path. The two-way strip of concrete from the main road to Montpelier was just the same though the ruts between the strips were deeper and certainly the braying of the donkeys louder. The names on the mini-taxis were even more exotic and a new road traversed across the west-facing slope of Nevis Peak, so it was possible to drive to Pinney's Beach without having to go through Charlestown. The capital boasted two supermarkets and the occasional visiting cruise ship. Nevis was flourishing.

Another second museum, The Nelson Museum, had opened. Though in most respects devoted to the *noble memory*, it contained displays about early Nevis and there were fresh archives. The conditions under which the staff operated were by no means favourable: funds were low; people required training; academic terms being what they were, volunteer helpers could mostly only come in the humid, hurricane months of July and August. Yet many distinguished academics – archaeologists, historians, sociologists – from both England and America had visited Nevis and had devoted several months determining exactly what existed and helping the custodians catalogue the records systematically. I went to study them the very next day.

The Nelson Museum is situated on a small knoll just near the old Bath Hotel – itself near the hot springs. Though there had been some plans to restore the hotel to its former glory, it now housed government offices.

I parked my car in the shade of a tree, walked up the steps to the small verandah and entered the Museum. On my right was a counter with brochures and booklets. Behind the counter a welcoming Nevisian suggested that I could either pay a small entrance fee or join the Friends of the Museum – which I promptly did. Having told her of my interest in the archives she introduced me to the archivist who took me into her office. Once again, I mentioned my interest not only in Philippa, but in some of the early settlers who had come to Nevis from Bristol. She invited me to go through into the working room and she would bring me the book I needed.

The archive room is minute – a tiny triangle of hot space with a small built-in table set by the window. Between taking notes I kept wiping moisture from my hands, trying not to mess up the documents.

I started working systematically through *Bristol & America*, a book that listed the first settlers sailing from the city to the Caribbean and the North American colonies, between 1654 and 1685. This had been published with the special permission of the Corporation of the City and it was easy to imagine the Lord Mayor in robes and gold chain, solemnly intoning this favour. I also learnt that when Bristol established an Archives Department in 1924, two other volumes, *Servants to Foreign Plantations*, were miraculously discovered in an old, dusty room. All the records went back to 1552, when, in the reign of Edward VI, Bristol's first Council House was built in Corn Street.

Once the Council House was up and running the Mayor attended early every morning for the transaction of city business and a record of everything that transpired was hurriedly written down in rough entry books by the appointed clerks. The Mayor's Court decisions were entered at the front of the book, details of the City's apprentices at the back.

However, around 1654, in the time of Cromwell's Protectorate, a third type of entry was added. Following orders from London, all apprentices – not just local ones – were now listed in the *Actions and Apprentices Rough Entry Books*. Moreover, Bristol's City Council also ordained that every servant going overseas had to be formally articled before embarkation. The two volumes of *Servants to the Foreign Plantations* that I was now examining were the fair copies of those compulsory enrolment lists.

The reason for such detailed, binding requirements was to prevent scandals. Some nine year earlier on 9th May 1645, a Parliamentary Ordinance ordered the Marshals of the Admiralty and the Cinque Ports to make thorough searches of all ships. The Officers and Justices were required to be '*very diligent in apprehending persons concerned in the kidnapping of children for overseas servitude*'.

But clearly the ordinance was widely ignored, for nine years later the Protectorate issued a second one. In view of the continuing and numerous complaints of kidnapping, and in order to '*prevent more mischief, all boys, maids and other servants which for the future shall be transported beyond the seas as servants shall, for their going shipboard, have their Covenants or Indentures of Service and Apprenticeship enrolled in the Tolzey Books – as other indentures of apprenticeships are and have to be used*'. The Tolzey Books were the Council books I was now studying.

In addition, the Water Bailiff of every port was required to make a thorough search of all ships for any passengers not registered and this time the Ordinance had teeth. If the Master carried a passenger who was not enrolled, he would be fined £20 for each person. Five pounds went to the person who had informed the Water Bailiff and the balance to the poor.

These enrolment entries were a gold mine, for their detail was extensive, containing not only the servants' names but where they came from, the date of their enrolment, their destination, their master's name and the length and conditions of service.

While apprentices working in Bristol were bound for seven to nine years, servants going to foreign parts were bound for only four or five. When their time was up, they were promised land, or money, or a house and an axe, double apparel and sufficient supplies to last the first year, which was expected to be lean. Such promises supposedly guaranteed the establishment of new settlements, but they were rarely kept. So while indentured servants might ultimately be given a small plot of land, few ever gained independence and generally they had a very hard time.

I could hardly credit the statistics. In the thirty years between 1654 and 1685, ten thousand emigrants had sailed to foreign lands from Bristol alone and they came from all over the British Isles. One even came from Burgundy in France.

These ten thousand people had 'elected' to begin a new life in the West Indies or America. They were of all classes, not all dirt poor, not all indentured servants. Some were landed gentry ruined by the Civil War, others were farmers, tradesmen, mechanics, husbandmen. Some left for what they considered was their own good, others for what the authorities considered was the country's good. Azariah Pinney, after whom the famous seven-mile stretch of sandy beach on Nevis is named, was one. During the Monmouth rebellion in 1685 he had elected to fight against King James II. After Monmouth's defeat, Pinney faced execution or life imprisonment. Evidence suggests that he bought himself off, but he still had to go to Nevis. He did spectacularly well and by the time he died was extremely wealthy.

Others were sent simply because they were in the wrong place at the wrong time. At the Bloody Assizes following the Rebellion, Judge Jeffreys sentenced most rebels to death. But over eight hundred were given to favoured people at Court and sold into slavery to work on the West Indian sugar plantations. Amongst the eight hundred were four young girls from Taunton. When Monmouth came through the town, they had been forced to embroider his standard under the watchful eyes of his soldiers. This was considered consorting with the enemy and there was no appeal. So these twelve-year-old children were snatched from their homes and ended up thousands of miles away from their families.

Without women the new colonies could not survive. When in 1618, a ship sailed to Virginia carrying ninety maids, the Company offered special rewards to men who would marry them. Yet such was the shortage of women, the offer was totally superfluous and remained so. Shipload after shipload, girls sailed from England to be eagerly courted at the harbour by the crowds of settlers awaiting their arrival. Since the number seeking wives greatly outnumbered the maids that came, the women could pick and choose. Not only the young and handsome, but the old and homely, too, would find a husband, and though this female 'export' continued for years, the demand was always far greater than the supply. In the early years of Nevis's settlement there was only one woman for every fifteen men.

I searched the names carefully. Joane Norman of Ashwicke went to Nevis, as did Margaret Fferiz of Cane — where was that? — and Elisabeth Nachen of Bartly, Susan Lewis of Notely, Alice Hoell of Wells, Margaret Phillips of Garway, Ann Fuller of Ffron, Elisabeth Munday of Bristol, Rebecca Waites of Andover.

As I systematically scanned I kept careful count and calculated that during those crucial thirty-one years, approximately one hundred and eighteen women and four hundred and ninety-six men sailed from Bristol for Nevis and St Christopher. But not one single woman had the name of Philippa.

At the end of the afternoon, I was tired and discouraged but at least one thing was clear. Either Philippa came before 1654, or she was not a servant but a member of the aristocratic gentry, or had been kidnapped as a child and not enrolled by the ship's master, or was already married when she arrived or did not sail from Bristol. Otherwise her name would be in those records.

These conclusions were not really all that illuminating and suddenly the task seemed overwhelming. How, I asked myself irritably, could I ever have thought this was going to be easy? How could I expect to trace someone when the records have been burnt and I had no maiden name, no date of birth, no age at death, and didn't even know where her bones lay?

Yet by the next morning as the sun came up and Nevis exerted its usual magic, my mood altered yet again. I decided to focus on Philippa's first husband, Clement Prentis, and turned to another source.

Chapter Seven

A Tree of Ancestors

*"The history of all the Caribbean group is so replete with
romantic episodes, and with such momentous military and naval
actions, that no apology is necessary for an endeavour to record,
and rescue from oblivion, anything of interest about them."*

§

V. Langford Oliver, *Preface to first Volume of 'Caribbeana'*

St Nicholas's Church, Bristol carries a panel sacred to the memory of Richard
Oliver, who died in 1708. He was a planter on Antigua, a Colonel of the
Militia and a member of Her Majesty's Council. His grandson of the same
name, who died at sea somewhere off Nevis on 16th April 1784, is also
commemorated. Though an MP for the City of London, he was a firm
supporter of the constitutional rights of the American colonies.

One hundred and thirty-five years later one of their descendants, Vere
Langford Oliver, who was probably born on Antigua, commissioned the
panel, dedicating it to *'his Ancestors and Kinsfolk who lie buried in the churchyard or
in their plantations'.*

Vere Oliver had inherited sufficient wealth to lead the life of a gentleman
of leisure. But while others would build grand houses, buy racing studs or
gamble, he spent twenty-five years collecting all the information he could
about families who lived in the British West Indies. These records, *The Caribbeana*,
first appeared in a quarterly magazine to subscribers only. Then he sought
financial help from friends and patrons to complete the work, though was not
always successful in raising the funds. Nevertheless, the six volumes he
assembled are now in the Bodleian Library, Oxford, and in 2005 were published
on compact disc.

When the archivist at the Nelson Museum brought me photocopies of his Nevis pages I returned to my investigation with renewed confidence. Soon I was completely enthralled by Oliver's material while offering heartfelt thanks that he had chosen to devote time and money to the task. Given the destruction of the Nevis Court Records, I never expected to be burrowing in such a gold mine. For he had searched wills, court cases, disposition of lands, instructions to brothers, sisters, attorneys, agents. Since his family owned extensive land on Nevis — now part of the Four Seasons Hotel on Pinney's Beach — he recorded a great deal about the island and all too soon a multitude of intriguing questions threatened to divert me from my main investigation.

How on earth did a transcript of the Parish Register of St George's, Nevis, end up in Fulham Palace, the home of the Bishop of London? How did the earliest will from St Kitts, dated 23rd September 1628, written by Robert Barwicke while sailing for England on *The Plough* of London, survive at all? He left his wife Margaret, who remained in Southampton, thirty pounds. Generous one might think, but this actually was her own money that had come from her mother! His bounty also extended to:

'*Master Captain Thomas Warner*' who had been '*verie kind and loving unto me and hath benne the cause by whom I have gotten my estate*'.

'*In testimonie therefore of my thankfulness . . . . I do give and bequeath unto him one Beaver hatt of the best kind which I humblie entreat him to weare for my sake to be given unto him within one month next after his arrival in England*'.

What exactly had Thomas Warner done to deserve a *Beaver hatt*?

Barwicke's will, identifying his land on Nevis, was very complicated — as most inevitably were, given that the boundaries of the land were never clearly defined. Fiscal matters, too, were equally tortuous and before long my head was spinning. The lawyers sorting out the estates made a killing.

Yet the best nugget of all was a case in the London Chancery Court. This was brought by one Thomas Litleton, a London merchant and entrepreneur, who seemed to have been a perpetual optimist, for he regularly underwrote voyages as far away as Turkey, Syria, the West Indies and Newfoundland. Around 1628 and in spite of many disastrous losses, he furnished three ships with *'meal, bread, victualls, municon apparrell'* and other necessary goods to the value of £5000 – about £75,000 in today's currency. The Governor of Nevis, Antonie Hilton, had already agreed the prices to be paid and the cargo arrived safely. Accordingly, John Procter, Litleton's agent on the island, delivered the goods to the eighty planters who had placed orders. But when he tried to collect payment no one – save three – paid a single penny, not even the Governor! So in 1629 Litleton sued them all. However, one month later, one planter, Roland Bullock, admitted he had ordered goods worth £16 and paid up.

I was naturally far more interested in the names of the eighty planters than their fiscal probity. But I was devastated when no Clement Prentis was listed. So either he was not on the island at the time, or hadn't ordered anything from London, or had paid up, or was one of the names recorded as 'blank'. I remember well my familiar feeling of impotence. I left the cramped archive room and walked in the museum grounds – a short distance from the Bath Springs. Who were those eighty planters? Where did they come from? Why didn't they pay? Who did they marry? How many managed to marry at all?

I was now thoroughly frustrated for I believed I had absolutely no hope of finding from local records when Clement Prentis or Philippa had arrived. But I forced myself back into the small, hot room and changed direction for the third time. I began scanning all the pages of *The Caribbeana*, noting down every single reference to Saddle Hill and luckily there were several.

Wills revealed that Saddle Hill lands had indeed been worked from the earliest years. Other names appeared when in 1677 a Census was taken and all able-bodied men on Nevis were formed into brigades ready to counter invasion threats from the French. The Quakers refused to be conscripted and were consequently persecuted.

I scanned these names but while there was no Clement Prentis, there was a William Phillips – presumably Philippa's second husband – listed in Captain Burr's division. So clearly Philippa's first husband was already dead. Better still, a Roger Prentis – perhaps Philippa's and Clement's son – was registered in Captain Thomas Butler's division.

In a second Census taken thirty years later, in 1707, I found a possible grandson, Edward Prentis. He was listed as head of a household that held one white male, four white females, six black males and two black females.

Suddenly the discoveries came on fast, as a Sarah, then Ann and a second Roger Prentis were recorded. Prentises were still working Saddle Hill land in the eighteenth century when a likely great-grandson was living up there. For in 1735, Edward Prentis had contributed forty-eight Negro working days towards the construction of a fortress high up on the southern slope of Saddle Hill.

Like Theseus in the Minotaur's tomb, I now followed the threads through time using Oliver's *Caribbeana* as my guide. I even found Prentises one hundred and thirty-four years after Philippa had died, in the Nevis Slave Register of 1817. But to learn more about them, I would have to delve into records in England and if I were to be successful I would need professional help.

Nevertheless, I knew now that without a shadow of doubt, Prentises had persisted on Nevis long after Philippa was dead. But for how long? The current telephone directory was an obvious place to look and in it I found nearly forty Prentises, their name spelt in a variety of ways. But fascinating as this indeed was, I was once again in a cul-de-sac – centuries and generations away from my starting point of Clement and Philippa. In truth I was no closer to knowing who they really were.

Chapter Eight

Savouring Success

"But the Thames is liquid history."

§

John Burns, *Oral Tradition*

I am not easily discouraged, but during a period of reflective wakefulness that night, admitted that now I really was. Gloom was too strong a word, pessimism more apt — a mood provoked by information which, though intriguing and clearly important, was horribly haphazard. True, I had found William Phillips, Philippa's second husband, and one husband out of two was not a bad score. True, I had seen that likely descendants of Clement and Philippa could be traced for generations. But the woman who had first captured Roland Archibald's devotion and then my fascinated interest, was rapidly receding down the corridors of time. Disembodied, out of focus, Philippa and Clement remained wraiths, tantalisingly out of grasp. Yet they haunted my dreams.

I feel guilty when I become discouraged for I know that facts are like fine jewels and every piece of information — no matter how small — adds to the final picture. But I still couldn't even see its outline. These two people had certainly lived on Nevis, but did they really work in the settlement that David Rollinson believed had been on Saddle Hill?

So when two pieces of excellent evidence turned up, separated historically by three hundred and sixty years, my mood changed to high excitement. Like the very best evidence, they came from unsuspected and unlikely sources.

By now the ownership of Montpelier Plantation Inn had changed hands. Devotees like myself, who had been going regularly for years, were apprehensive when we learnt that an American family, the Hoffmans, were to take over. We had slipped into the Inn's ambience and company so comfortably that our visits were like slipping into a favourite coat. No matter how old and worn, we loved it. But James and Celia had given most of their lives to its creation and their two children, Charles and Anna, whom I had known since they were respectively a toddler and baby, were now fully mature adults. We all were beginning to show our age; so too – if truth be told – was Montpelier. We might tremble at the prospect of a facelift but it would do a power of good to the cottages and the grounds.

One of the great strengths of the place had not only been the skill with which James and Celia had created and run one of the nicest small hotels anywhere, but the fact that with one or two exceptions the entire staff had been there forever. One critical question was would they remain? We were all reassured when we received a note from the new owners, that all they intended to do was tweak a few things here and there – and in essence that's exactly what happened.

When I came not long after they had taken over, there were three new faces in reception and in the office. There was a fresh toddler, Kyler, the first child of Timothy and Meredith's, a firm, delightful, active character who knew his own mind, adored by all. There was air conditioning in the rooms and everything had been splendidly spruced up. The view to Saddle Hill was as enticing as ever and though I could still walk up there it took me rather longer. The view of course, was as beautiful, Roland Archibald's house even more dilapidated. Yet the seventeenth century ponds still held water, though there were more lilies growing inside, and I always felt how lucky Brett had been, for I never actually saw the osprey. The carving on Philippa's tomb was becoming more weathered; the path up to the Saddle Hill barracks had been cleared and a small tourist kiosk had been built with information and drinks for the passing traveller. But this did not survive long, for a nasty land dispute erupted between two land owners over access and rights. Many feared that if this were prolonged there could be damage even to the tomb itself.

Luther, too, was still going strong but in yet another index of Nevis's increasing prosperity, he had a brand new car which he kept in pristine condition and drove with the utmost care.

The island was flourishing and attracting many celebrities. John Travolta would come on his yacht; Oprah Winfrey was his guest from time to time and allegedly loved the island. The BBC made a film there; so too did Tony Robinson in *Time Team* covering an excavation on a site in an old sugar plantation, inland from the Four Seasons golf course. Yet I felt the discoveries, though fascinating, were not likely to be as rewarding as those that would be revealed when work was undertaken on land near Saddle Hill. For up there no wholesale planting or building had ever taken place, no roads driven through and no houses put up, so evidence from past centuries would have remained untouched and undisturbed.

Yet this would be the year when the crucial clue emerged. One part was so simple that I berated myself for having been so stupid for so long.

§

One day I had to go down to the Administration offices to renew my visitor's permit. I was ushered into the office of Mrs Averil Richard-Williams, Head of the Visa Section. In a cool, breezy room in the beautiful, old Bath Hotel I sat opposite a slim, middle-aged lady, who was speedily dispatching administrative business with a friendly competence that I greatly admired.

While waiting for a signature to be put on a form, we chatted and soon the conversation turned to the regularity and duration of my visits and the puzzle of Philippa's marker stone on Saddle Hill. Everyone knew about it, volunteered Mrs Williams, but sadly Mr Archibald, the one person who alone knew how it came there, was now dead. On the other hand, she volunteered, had I heard of Mr Herman Ward, now ninety-six years old, and still tending his own garden. He had been born in Cox Village just below Saddle Hill and would likely know a great deal about the story.

Since she attended the same Methodist church as Mrs Hyleta Liburd, Herman Ward's daughter, she was sure that a meeting could be arranged and gave me a contact number. I was delighted. Oral evidence would be a welcome respite from delving deep into dusty documents.

While having tea in the pool bar that afternoon, I mentioned to some friends that I hoped to meet a ninety-six year old man who lived all his life nearby. One of the gardening staff, Junior, who was forty-five but looked twenty-five, and had looked twenty-five ever since I first met him years back — was quietly enjoying a beer. Shyly, he approached.

"Pardon, Dr June, but I overhead. Mr Ward is my grandfather," he said. "Meeting him can easily be arranged."

Eddie, the barman, now joined in.

"I attend the same church as his daughter and I'll help arrange this."

Two days later, after Eddie had finished work, he met me in the car park. Armed with notebook and pencil I climbed into his truck and off we went along the bumpy concrete. At the main road, he turned left, drove half a mile, then stopped outside a wooden house painted in pale orange and dark tan, set back from the road. The gate opened into a small garden of flowers, vegetables and herbs.

Eddie tapped on the glass pane of the front door. The curtain behind was drawn back and a middle-aged woman with a warm, smiling face, wearing spectacles, opened the door.

"Welcome, welcome," she said. "Come in, please."

I stepped into a small room. There was a sofa on the left, two chairs and a small table on the right. Beyond was another door — also with a curtained pane of glass.

"Please sit down," said Mrs Liburd. "My father will be out directly."

She disappeared into the back room. There were a few sounds, then the door opened.

"Dad," she said, "I want you to meet Dr June who is staying at Montpelier. Eddie, of course, you've known for years."

I stepped forward and shook hands with a man about five feet seven inches, whose bearing and dignity belied his age. His muscles were still strong, as the strength of his handshake revealed. One fact alone betrayed his years: his left eye was clearly painful. He and his daughter sat down on the sofa; Eddie and I sat opposite on the chairs. I was thankful that Eddie had offered to take notes, for not only would he know the spellings, but would also be familiar with the accent which at times I find hard to understand. Being very deaf doesn't help at all.

"I gather you know Saddle Hill well, Mr Ward?"

"Yes. I've walked over it all my life."

Not wishing to tire him, I decided to get straight to business. "Your grandson, Junior, has told you that I've been trying to find out about the tomb and the tablet up there. I understand it was built by Mr Archibald?"

"Yes," he replied quietly, "so I was told."

"Sir, when Mr Archibald was building the house, do you remember him building the tomb?"

The reply was unambiguous. "No. I only knew he was building the house. I didn't go up there at that time."

"So you didn't hear any talk about finding the tablet or bones underneath the tomb?"

His reply was even more emphatic. "No, nothing like that at all."

Everyone fell silent and that seemed to be that.

But I felt it would be rude to leave at this point. Eddie and Mr Ward's daughter had gone to a great deal of trouble to arrange the meeting and anyway I warmed to this dignified man, as I had to Mr Archibald. There could not be many people on Nevis whose birth date had preceded World War I, who would have seen the fortune of the island ebb and flow over ninety-six years.

"May I ask you where you were born, sir?" I now asked.

"In Cox Village, just below Saddle Hill."

"And what did you do for your work?"

"I was a stonemason," he said. "I was a stonemason long before they had any machines. I did all the facing and the dressing by hand."

Eddie interjected. "He dressed the stones that support the main gates at Montpelier."

Mr Ward nodded and smiled again, looking pleased and proud. "I did."

"How long were you at school?"

"Until I was about eleven – perhaps twelve." He turned towards his daughter who put her arm over his shoulder. They chatted rapidly but I couldn't understand a single word.

"Probably about fourteen!" she said finally.

"And did you go immediately into stonemasonry?"

"No, that was much later. To begin with I worked on Prentis Works."

I forced myself to stay very still for I had nearly jumped clean out of the chair. But I took a deep breath and then said quietly. "In England, the word 'works' generally means a factory, or perhaps a brick works, or something like that. Is that what you mean?"

"No," he replied and for the first time his tone was a tad impatient. "Prentis Works means Prentis land – on Saddle Hill."

"Where on the hill is it?" I asked.

"You have to go south. Up over from Cox Village then way, way south. We got to it from the east side of Saddle Hill, walking over Macfarlane's land first. But it's all covered over with scrub now."

"What were you doing at Prentis Works?"

"We were growing cotton. Harry Ransom was the overseer. He was overseer at Montpelier too. He was a tough one."

"Were you a share cropper?" I asked.

"To begin with we all were. But that stopped around the 1950s, I think." Again he chatted with his daughter. "We soon realised that it was better to pay rent for land than to work for someone else and give them over half of everything we grew."

"Coming back to Prentis Works. Is there anything else you remember?"

"There was an old building on it. We used to store the cotton in there."

"Was it a sugar mill?"

"No, just a very, very old building."

I turned to Mrs Liburd. "Could we – in our mind's eye as it were – go up the road from Montpelier to Saddle Hill and perhaps your father could indicate where the path went off to Prentis Works."

This was not a satisfactory exercise. For if Mr Ward had not been up on Saddle Hill since before Roland Archibald built his house, that meant he hadn't been up there for well over thirty years. Eddie admitted he'd never been up there at all! Moreover, the road that I was describing was new and there were no obvious signs I could offer Mr Ward that might match those in his mind's eye.

Nevertheless, though I came away with only one certainty, it was the most important of all. Prentis Works – lands on Saddle Hill, way up and south of Cox Village – were enshrined in the living, oral tradition of Nevis and had to be in the land deeds. Why had I had never thought to search for the name there? Mostly because in all my years I had never heard the name mentioned – only Saddle Hill. Nor were Prentis Works mentioned in the *Caribbeana*.

When the conversation had drawn to a natural end, I began to rise. Hearing me move, Mr Ward shot to his feet.

"He's always like that," said his daughter, admiringly. "Aren't you, Dad? First on his feet every time."

"I'm not surprised," I said. "He's so fit."

"He's a great example for you, Eddie," said Mrs Liburd.

Eddie grinned bashfully.

§

Back at the hotel, I tackled Junior again. "I had a lovely meeting with your grandfather. But tell me, when you were herding goats on Saddle Hill, what land were you on?" I asked.

The answer was immediate. "Why, Prentis Works of course."

Once again, I was stunned. I simply couldn't believe what I was hearing.

§

Next day was the hotel's weekly barbecue on the beach – a highly popular event. Everyone came, from guests and the Chef, the staff and the entire Hoffman family including the two-year-old Kyler, who stole the show as he lay face down in the sand and stuffed handfuls of the gorgeous stuff into his mouth.

Since everyone always chatted to him, he was happy to be passed on from person to person. So in turn I was handed the adorable parcel who pulled my nose and covered my front with sand. Finally, he was carried to the tap for a good wash.

Meanwhile I strolled over for a chat with Sandy, who had been at Montpelier for thirty-five years. He was always at the beach party because he was both the best barbecuer on the island and the best bowler in the cricket team.

Playing after lunch on the strip of grass just above the sand, leg-side fielders at mid-wicket stand up to their waists in warm sea water. The ball is a tennis ball, the bat a heavy piece of carved wood, the wicket a chair. Sandy's hands are so huge that he can hide three balls in them and let them all go simultaneously. The batsman becomes schizophrenic and generally misses all three, one of which will hit the chair. "Howzatt?" Most definitely out!

While Eddie was setting up the bar and Sandy heating the charcoal, away in the distance an outraged Kyler was yelling furiously, as, with proper West Indian firmness, his nanny held him under the cold-water tap and washed every particle of sand out of every single crevice. Suddenly all fell quiet as he was wrapped in a towel.

"Dr June," volunteered Eddie, "Sandy knows Saddle Hill real well. You should talk to him."

I strolled over to the grill, but now I knew what Sandy would say. "Sandy, I gather you know Saddle Hill?"

"Yes. Before I ever came to Montpelier I worked up there, picking cotton."

Once again I became very still. "Where on Saddle Hill?"

"Prentis Works," he said.

"If I draw a rough map," I said, "could you place Prentis Works for me?"

"Sure. Just as soon as the fire is going properly."

I drew out a notebook, set the page sideways and drew the twin peaks of Saddle Hill with Roland Archibald's house on the ridge. Then Sandy began to trace a line on my map.

"We didn't get there by going up the present track," he volunteered, "we went right round to the east – on the Atlantic side."

"But suppose you're now standing by the house, and you're looking south, exactly where are Prentis Works?" I asked.

"Upper Prentis is where the tomb is. Lower Prentis is a bit further down – below the house to the south-west. You've got to go down and up a little valley. There was an old storage building down in the valley. But that's where Prentis Works is all right."

I remembered the path down to a valley where David had found the pottery shards.

Next morning at the hotel, another gardener, Miller Pemberton, owner of Coco the donkey, greeted me.

"You've been wanting to know about Prentis Works," he said.

"Yes."

He led me to where we could see Saddle Hill and held his arms out wide. "Go up to Mr Archibald's house. To the left and below is all Prentis Works. He had a heap of land did Mr Archibald. He owned all of Prentis. Between the house and an old wall on the right hand side is a road. If you go down about a hundred feet, though I doubt you can because it'll be so overgrown, and swing towards the right into the grassland, you'll come to a big cedar tree. Just below that there's a building that was used by Mr Archibald for sheltering his cattle. Lower Prentis is about one hundred and twenty feet to the left. Doctor's Bottom is about three hundred feet further south from that building and when you've crossed Doctor's Bottom, you can go on up Morton Hill."

I was thrilled, for Miller's description corresponded to where David and Brett had placed the old settlement. "We found the old wall. You know about the tomb, don't you?"

"Of course."

"Was there anything else up there – bones, perhaps?" I said hopefully.

"No, no bones."

Then, gloriously – unexpectedly – the second piece of evidence came in and I could finally make a plausible guess about Philippa's age.

§

I spent the morning of the next day making notes for a short talk on the Philippa mystery. Some old friends and new guests had requested a briefing so my audience gathered on the terrace where tea was being served. Finn, a charming small boy, the eldest son of other friends, politely offered to carry my notes, but I only had a single piece of paper. However, I asked him to pass round the artefacts that David Rollinson had found.

Perched on a stool, I told the story very concisely, since there were lawyers in the audience. I detailed the paths I had recently followed and what I had managed to unravel.

There were questions; there were offers to help. One guest had a son who had married into an East Anglian family of Prentises, whose ancestors had emigrated to America in the seventeenth century and might have a connection with Clement. As I moved down off my stool, Finn's father, James, stood up.

"Thank you so much," he said. "I think refreshments are called for."

As Eddie and Garfield came around to take orders, someone from the office came up and handed me an envelope. "This just came in for you, Dr June."

The long e-mail had been sent from Bristol by David Small and his wife. I read it once, twice, then a third time, disbelief turning to relief and finally excitement.

"June."

I didn't hear James speak. I was miles away. "Uh... what? I'm so sorry!" Pulled back from the seventeenth century, I saw James by my side.

"June, what can I get you?"

I didn't hesitate for a second and with outrageous impertinence said "Champagne, please."

Others were listening and gathered around. I have no idea who it was – Lincoln, I think – but someone gazed at me keenly, hesitated, then guessed. "You've found Philippa!"

"I think we may have. This just arrived from Bristol. I can't quite take it in. I searched over one thousand names in the Bristol records but didn't find a single Philippa. David and Christine searched about twelve thousand names in the Hotten index and found two!" I now read the e-mail for the third time. "One Philippa was buried in Barbados in 1679, so can't be ours. But the second Philippa swore an Oath of Allegiance before sailing from Dartmouth to St Christopher. The date is about right, too – 1634. It has to be her."

I passed the email around and raised my glass.

§

A list of the names and surnames of those psons wch are bound for
St Christophrs & haue taken the oath of Allegeance before Mr William Gourney, Maior:
of Dartmouth they beinge brought befor me the Twentyeth day of February
in ye Yeare of or lord god 1634

Imprimis WILLIAM HAUKINS of Exon A Glover Aged 25 yeares or thereabouts
JAMES COURTNEY of Exon A Blacksmith Aged 23 Years or thereabouts
RICHARD SKOSE of Newton Abbot A Seafaringe man 37 Years or thereabouts
FRANCIS BOYCE of London A Button hole maker aged 25 Yeares or thereabouts
WILLIAM CARKILLE of Plimouth A Saylemaker aged 21 Years or thereabouts
WILLIAM GURGE of Exon a Shoemaker aged 20 Yeares or thereabouts

ALCE WHITMORE of Huniton in Devon Spinster Aged 25 Years or thereabouts
PHILIPP* STEPHENS of Ashberton in Devon Spinster Aged 28 Yeares or thereabouts
SARA COOSE of Exon Spinster aged 18 Years or therabouts
JUDITH STEVENS of Exon Spinter [Spinster] aged 19 Years or therabouts
MARGARETT HARWOOD of Stoke-gabriell in Devon spinster Aged 22 Years
or therabouts
EDWARD MORRIS of Exon a Locker aged 21 years or therabouts
THOMAS BRYANT of Bampton in Devonshire a husbandman aged 23 Years
or therabouts
WILLYAM MAY of Mynard in Somersett a sea man aged 32 Yeares or therabouts
HUTINNE OWETH of St Steevens in Cornwall a husbandman Aged 24.
JOHN WILLS in Barnstable in Devon a Feltmaker Aged 35 Years or thereabouts
SYMON WEEKS of Exon a Worsted weaver aged 16 years or thereabouts
THOMAS JERMAYNE of Exon an Ostler aged 30 Years.
JOHN FRENCH of Washford in Ireland a seaman 26 years.
WILL^m HILL of great Torington in Devonshire a husbandman Aged 28 Years.
JOHN HOCKSLEY of Stoke Cannon in Devon a Tayler aged 28 Years.
JAMES ROSMAN of London a husbandman aged 21 years.
ELIZABETH REED of Exon a Spinster aged 19 Years or thereabouts.
MARY HARTE of Lyme a Spinster aged 18 Years or there abouts.
MARY HOPPINE of Exmister a spinster aged 20 Yeares.
MARYES HARRIES of Stoke Pommeroy in Devon aged 23 Years or thereabouts.
ELIZABETH QUICKE of Barnstable in Devon aged 18 Years.
ELIZABETH HILL of Brixam in Devon aged 24 Years.
JOANE SHORTE of Exon Aged 20 Yeares.
JOANE LANNERS [or LAUERS] of Modbury in Devon aged 19 Years.
JANE GOULDINGE of St Thom. the Apostle in Devon aged 16 years or thereabouts.

JAMES WORTHY

Deputy

For Mr THOROUGHGOOD

---

* Footnote written by the recorder says, 'probably intended for Philippa.'

Later that night delighted though I was, I remember cautiously ticking off on my fingers the facts about which I was reasonably confident.

Firstly, from the Oath that I had just read, I knew when Philippa left England, where she came from and roughly her age. Though she sailed in February or March 1634, she probably arrived in St Christopher (St Kitts) around June 1635, but she didn't take fifteen months to get there – three and a half, more likely. For the Julian calendar was still in use and the New Year started in April. Secondly, there were at least eighty planters on Nevis at that time and Clement was very likely one of them.

Thirdly, though by 1677, he was dead, Philippa's second husband, William Phillips, was listed in one brigade and her son, Roger Prentis, in another. Fourthly, she died on 11th August 1683 and her marker stone was carved in Jamestown. fifthly, records from early in the next century reveal four grandchildren – Sarah, Edward, Ann and Roger. Sixthly, in 1735, a great-grandson, Edward, was working land on Saddle Hill. Seventhly, the family clearly made their mark, because even today their land is known as Prentis Works. Finally, one hundred years later the Prentises were still on Nevis and over three hundred years later, there were still many Prentises in the telephone book.

I still had a great deal to research and would begin with a systematic search of the National Archive in the Public Record Office at Kew. I would seek help from my youthful friend and colleague, young Peter Robinson and ask David Small and Christine to confirm any fresh facts I found. I would visit Ashburton and meet with local historians. All this was to take another full year. Yet one day I took a deep breath and adopting a stance that not all academic historians would applaud – through some might – I wrote a reconstruction of Philippa's life.

Nevis Peak (top) and Saddle Hill (above)

6

17th century ponds (above and right)

7

17th century shelters (top and above)

17th century cistern (top) and water cooler (above)

Interior of the Hermitage Hotel (above)

Lime kilns (above, right and opposite)

18th century sugar mill (above)

Vince Hubbard with Sandy Claxton

Herman Ward

David Rollinson

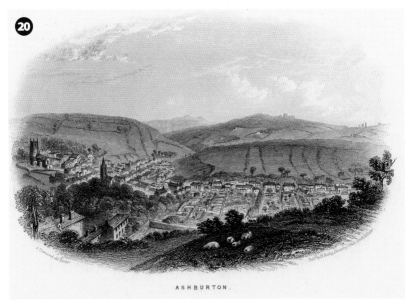

ASHBURTON.

St Andrew's Church, Ashburton, with Dartmoor in the background (above)

Dartmouth in 1619 (top and above)

St Kitts from Pinneys Beach (top) and pottery shards found on Prentis Works (above)

26

434 Nº 434

115   Brought over   85247 3 10

For   59 8 10

A like Debenture in the Name of Roger Prentis,
Elizabeth Austin, Ann Brown and Sarah Prentis
of Nevis Inhabitants for the Sum of Fifty Nine
pounds Eight Shillings & tenn pence. Dated the 29.th of
April 1713. And signed

Phil: Meadows
Robt Monckton
T: Foley

Received of the Lords Commissioners
of Trade & Plantations ye abovementioned
Debenture by virtue of a Letter of Attorny
from the said Eliz: Austin, Ann Brown
and Sarah Prentis Dated in Nevis the 7.th of
Novemr 1712. Witness Our hands this 22d
of Decr 1713   Joseph Kerr
286 — 354   Dan: Offord

Prentis compensation claims (above and right)

27

Decemr the 22.d 1713

These are to Certify the Rt Honoble the Lords
Commissioners of Trade & Plantations
or whom Else it may concern that I
Matthew Vanhalmael of the Island
of Nevis was very well acquainted
with Roger Prentis of Nevis Planter
returnd as a joynt Sufferers by the French
Invasion of that Island in 1705 6 with
Austin, Brown &c and that the sd
Roger Prentis went on a Voyage from
Nevis bound for London about the year
1707 or 1708, in the Ship called the Martha
John Mather Commander of London &
that the said Prentis or Ship Martha
has not since that time been heard of
at Nevis but is genrally believed by
all People to be lost & perished with
all the People on Board her. Witness
my hand.
= M Vanhalmael

78

*Roland Archibald in 1977 (top) and shortly
before his death (left)*

The village of Hazelton (above and right)

Eliza Prentise's gravestone (above)

Part Two

"And the past is not static. It can be relived only in memory,
and memory is a device for forgetting as well as remembering.
It, too, is not immutable. It re-discovers, reinvents, reorganises."

§

P D James: *Time to Be in Earnest: a Fragment of Autobiography.*

Chapter Nine

Days That Have Gone By

*'a plantation can never flourish until families be planted with
the respect of wives and children and fix the people on the soyle'*

§

anon 1609

She had many reasons for forgetting and little time for remembering. Besides, memory could play tricks. As a child her only certainty had been that she was born in Ashburton, would likely marry in Ashburton and die in Ashburton. Though the river Derte just outside the town flowed through Totnes and onto Dartmouth and the sea, her boundaries were strictly limited – those of a community on the south-eastern fringe of Dartmoor. Horizons beyond were unimaginable.

Born in 1607, she was the second child of Richard Stephens and Jane Jorden. Her father worked in the mines up on the moor and the family was dirt poor. Though people spoke of prosperous days over a hundred years ago when the Ashburton stannary – one of just four in the Southwest – accounted for forty percent of all the tin mined in Devon, the industry was now in serious decline. Little metal was being mined, working conditions for the men were appalling and their wages pitiful.

So memory never obliterated that fact that life was a constant struggle. There was never a time when she was not working. If she and her mother were not searching for food, then preparing meals, they were washing clothes, or walking to the weekly market to buy whatever wool they could afford. They would card the wool at home and make yarn that would be sold the next week. Whatever coins a weaver might give them would be used to buy more wool – in a never-ending chain of labour that could snap at any time. Just one break could precipitate a crisis – and it did.

She was just six when her father fell sick and could work only intermittently. To her mother's shame – that she remembered well – they were forced to apply for Poor Relief. In 1613, Richard Stephens received three shillings for his wife and children. Then a year later her father just disappeared. They asked around but never learnt whether he had gone up to the moor and died or had walked to Dartmouth or Exeter to find work and decided never to return. In those years there were many such wandering vagrants. Once again, they survived only through parish handouts. During May and June 1614, her mother received 13s.6d. A final payment was made in July and that was the end.

Those were times Philippa preferred to forget and for almost sixty-eight years, forget them she did. Then her grandson, Roger, asked her a question and memories came flooding back with a clarity that both startled and amazed her.

§

She was old now: unremitting toil had etched lines on her face and the sun had weathered her skin. She still carried herself erect though, and as an admired matriarch – wife to two husbands, mother of two sons, grandmother of four grandchildren – she was regarded with awe. Since only a few lived to a great age her experience was unrivalled and there was no one else alive who had known Nevis in 1635. Many believed she had known no other life.

In most respects she was highly privileged for her family had wealth in land and sugar cane. There were servants to work in the house and slaves to work the fields; sons to supervise them and grandsons to learn. All were busily involved, all shared in their success. Yet now she had something that no one else had – time to remember.

The Christmas winds had set in and the air was cool. Every evening as the light faded, she would sit in the shelter of the house that Clement had built – down in the lee of Saddle Hill, some sixty feet or so below the hut where he had first taken her – and watch the sun sinking into the sea over the rippling fields of sugar cane. Known as Prentis Works, and the source of a security she could never have imagined, their land began on the ridge near the pond Clement had also built, and fell below to acres of fertile earth.

Sugar cane kept everyone busy from dawn until dusk. She believed they now owned at least fifty slaves though she had never counted them. Her son kept all the records. Apart from the women who worked in the house, she rarely met them either, for slaves lived and slept in rough huts in the fields below.

She sat quietly in her chair, listening to the familiar sounds of the evening meal being prepared. Hearing a step, she turned her head and saw Roger, her grandson, a youth in his late teens, carrying two pewter mugs.

"I knew I'd find you here," he said as he handed her one. The mug would hold Madeira wine diluted with water. None of the family had succumbed to the temptations of rum, thank God. She would have spoken her mind if they had!

"Thank you," she said. "But I didn't expect to see any of you boys. Surely the brigade is drilling this evening?"

"No, grandmother. That was yesterday. We were all there, my father and William."

"So what did you do today?"

"Oh, I was down at Charlestown. We have a shipment of sugar going to London this week and another going out in January. I was generally helping. I couldn't believe the paperwork."

"We've done well this year," she said.

"We worked hard for it, God knows," he replied. He sat on the wall, dug in his jerkin, found a pipe and filled it with tobacco, which, gingerly, he attempted to light. He had only recently begun smoking and hadn't yet quite mastered the knack.

She was pleased for the smoke kept the flies away. She looked at him with deep happiness, for she loved Roger well. She knew she should not have favourites but he was the image of his grandfather, with Clement's dark eyes, long, fair hair, and a tinge of red in the stubble on his chin. He had the same sturdy build, too, and the same obstinate strength but also a welcome gentleness.

"You're so like your grandfather. None of the others are."

"Am I? What was he like? When did you meet him? Where did you meet him?"

"So many questions, grandson. At Red Storehouse – on the jetty, actually."

"At Jamestown?"

"There was no Jamestown then."

"Well, at Charlestown?"

"There was no Charlestown, either — only a wooden building with a red roof called Red Storehouse. That was all that was there when I first met your grandfather."

"When was that?"

"May or June, 1634 or 1635, I think. I was never rightly sure. We had sailed a long time."

"Did you both come from the same part of England?"

"Oh, no! He was from places I had never known — way out to the east. They called it the Fen Country — a low and very flat land, he said. He believed his ancestors came from a country across the North Sea — Norway. His colouring, you see. My people were darker."

"So where did you come from?"

"Right the other side of England — a village in Devon, Ashburton."

Roger settled himself more comfortably. The pipe was pulling nicely and his pewter mug was still half full. "Start at the beginning, grandmother, and tell me."

Chapter Ten

The Land From Which We Sprang

"Here dead lie because we did not choose
To live and shame the land from which we sprung.
Life, to be sure, is nothing much to lose;
But young men think it is and we were young."

§

A E Housman, *More Poems*

For a while she was silent. Roger didn't press her but just waited patiently, scrutinising the weather-beaten face, the thin, white hair, the familiar, determined gaze. But there was a milky trace in her left eye and he sensed an ebbing of strength. He recognised the tell-tale signs for he had seen them often in the animals he tended. How much more time did she have?

Philippa was hesitant, not because of a reluctance to retrace the journey she had travelled, but because it was an effort to recall the small child, and the answers would be haphazard.

"We were very poor," she finally volunteered. "I had one brother. Our cottage was right at the end of North Street at the edge of the town – on the way to the moor."

Roger didn't know what a moor was, but wouldn't interrupt.

"But most days we would take another way in through Cad Lane."

"Why?" asked Roger, "was it shorter?"

"No, much longer." She gave a little grimace. "Some called it Shameface Lane. If you were poor, you tried to avoid the shops near the Bullring. We couldn't always pay our bills and the tradesmen would threaten us. Their shouting frightened me."

"I can't imagine anything frightening you, grandmother," he said.

"In those days many things frightened me," she said abruptly. "But when times were better, North Street was a nice way to walk home. The path ran along the banks of the river and there were cottages on either side."

She could see the small child skipping and running.

"After the cottages, the path wound round to the left and over a humped back bridge – Great Bridge. Then it curved round, still alongside the stream. In the spring time there were pretty yellow flowers on the banks and everything was so green. The water wasn't hot and smelly like at Bath Springs. It was dark, dark brown. Yet if you took it in your hand it looked crystal clear, but oh, it was so cold. In winter all the leaves fell off the trees and they were bare for months."

Roger was struggling; he couldn't conceive this at all.

"The worst days were in January when the days were dark. The sun never came up high and the winds blew the snow off the moors."

By now Roger was thoroughly confused. "What's snow?" he asked.

The question brought her up sharp. Even during the worst storms on Nevis, she had never even seen hail! How could she possibly describe snow to someone who had only known rain? Snow-white, icy, soft flakes tumbling out of the sky, whirling, turning, stinging, somersaulting, then building up in layers on the ground. It was so cold that you got chilblains, which she couldn't explain either. She made a great effort. Then she laughed to herself: particles of grated coconut tumbling from the sky would never do.

"I can't really explain," she admitted. "I don't really remember my father for we lost him when I was about six, I think. He just disappeared. Life was terrible. We lived on a few shillings from the Poor Relief and neighbours despised us. But we just had to get on with things. Luckily, the wool trade was good and I was taught a skill. We'd buy wool and sell the yarn to our cousins, the Weeks family. They were weavers and good to us after my father disappeared. We worked as one family."

"Like we do?" asked Roger.

"Just as we do. And I recollect some good times. The St Laurence Fair lasted for three days and all sorts of people came – peddlers from the big towns with their pack horses – others came from very far away. Even the women from the moor would come down.

"I remember an old gypsy woman giving me a remedy for an ailing cow. 'You cut a few hairs from the tail,' she said, 'and set them between a piece of bread and butter and give it to eat unto the first strange dog that cometh by. If the dog will eat the same then the cow shall recover; if he utterly refuses, the cow shall die.'

"She wanted me to cross her palm for her sovereign remedy. But I had nothing and she shouted at me. By then I wasn't afraid of anyone's curses. I just told her we had neither bread nor butter at home, nor cow neither and then ran off."

She laughed. "Once we had a sick cow up here so I told your grandfather the remedy. He said it was all nonsense and the only cure was fresh water and good grazing, and in any case there weren't any strange dogs around!"

She drank from her pewter mug, then turned it in her hands. "They made good pewter in Ashburton. This is all I still have from there. Except many memories ... and a few recipes."

"Which ones?" enquired Roger quietly.

"The sausage. They called it *Leche Lombard*, but I don't rightly know why. We made it on the eve of Corpus Christi, though it's way long since I've been to such church services. Takes a deal of work. You've seen me grinding the pork in a mortar with raw eggs, and sugar and salt and pepper. We used raisins and dates, but you can't get them here, so I use currants. We put the mixture in a bladder and it boiled in red wine, with ginger, cinnamon and saffron when we could get it, and added water from gillyflowers. We don't have them here either, so I use rose water. But it's not the same ..."

"It's still mighty good."

"Weddings were the best times because amusement was provided for all. I recall one real well. There was maypole on the Priggemead, with dancing and a scramble to catch the slippery pig. The town crier called for silence, the music stopped and the dancers left the ring. Then the pig was lathered with soft soap and turned loose.

"I was in a group of women on the edge of the crowd. Some had babes in their arms, others toddlers clinging to their skirts. The pig was a-squealing and a-squealing and ran so fast between one man's legs that he was knocked right over. So we women made a lane which the pig charged along, followed by scores of young men shouting and shoving. The pig tumbled into the river, then scrambled out and eventually came near us again. But this time we made a ring and hemmed it in.

"I never forgot that day. One young man stood to one side — strong and handsome he was. He just waited until everyone was mighty tired, the pig included. Then suddenly he jumped, caught the pig, forced his hands under its belly and they both rolled over and over in the mud. But he held on real tight and they landed at my feet. He was declared the winner."

The scene returned with great vividness — the noise, the mêlée, the crowds. She could see the young girl, long black hair caught in a kerchief, pink apple cheeks, smiling encouragement.

Then everything faded except the intense gaze of a victorious youth, who saw her laughing as he clung onto the pig for dear life. Suddenly, unaccountably, the pig surrendered and lay on top of the man as if they would sleep together. The man looked up; Philippa looked down. From behind the pig's ear she saw a human eye winking at her and felt a surge of excitement of a kind she had never before felt, at once both physical and spiritual.

"I knew then I would marry him," she said.

"And did you?" asked Roger.

"No, grandson. Within a twelve month, most everyone was dead."

Chapter Eleven

Living in Limbo

"It is better to fight for the good, than to raill at the ill;
I have felt with my native land, I am one with my kind,
I embrace the purpose of God and the doom assign'd."

§

Alfred Lord Tennyson, *Maud*

Jim Gye was reckoned a hard-working man, who would be a good father to the children she would bear him. Known to have a way with animals, he worked on a farm on Stawell's land but owned a small piece of ground – just large enough for one cow, some hens and a pig. They would have to work hard but would get by.

Everyone was very happy for Philippa. The marriage was set for Midsummer, so her Mother began hoarding a few things that she would take to her new home – pots, pans, a pewter mug – and the Weeks family began weaving her some cloth.

On the first day of the New Year, that began in April when winter had finally yielded to spring, it was now her turn to take part in the Lady-day ritual, celebrating the Annunciation of the Blessed Virgin.

She was excited so rose early, dressed quickly and walked the mile or so along North Street to the centre of Ashburton. There was no need to go down Shameface Lane for it was still dark and the shopkeepers in bed. Besides, they owed no one anything.

She remembered shivering in the cool morning air. There had been frost on the moor that night and the mist had poured down into the valleys. She walked fast for it was important to take up a good position by the well. If you saw the first rays of the sun reflected in the water, there would be good luck in your marriage.

The well was large. The water gushed up from a deep spring, then flowed away in a strong stream. Legend said that in the valley near Witton, the miners had defiled the river Yeo with tailings from the mine. These had poisoned the Ashburton springs so for years people who drank at the town pump got a distemper and fever. But then, so the story went, in their distress the townspeople made a vow to the Virgin – though Philippa had no idea what they had vowed. However, on the following Lady-day, a large spring of sweet water had burst out of the ground and gushed forth ever since.

She remembered kneeling with the other girls around the tall granite cross that stood on a six-sided plinth. The mist in the valley was burning off and soon the sun would be mirrored in the water. As the light began to appear, they took up their places by the pool, crouching low, watching for the sun's first rays. Those who understood such things crouched on the western side, so as to be the first to catch the light from the east. When they saw its reflection they would take a drop of water on a finger tip and cross themselves. Each girl had a small vessel by her side. If they were successful, they would fill this from the well and keep the water as a charm for the months to come.

Everyone became increasingly tense as the light deepened. The rays were about to cast their reflection when a dark cloud crossed over the rising sun. Philippa's hand dipped into a blackness which terrified her and all the girls. They spoke no words, but wrapping their shawls around their heads, hurried each to their home.

The year was 1625 and the country had a new king, Charles I, so they had felt that the omens were good. But moving rapidly up from Exeter, the plague struck fast and deep and in only a few days burials soared. Philippa's mother, brother and future husband were among the first to die. 1626 was even worse: four hundred and sixty-four people, out of a population of two thousand, were buried in Ashburton alone.

Traditionally there were only two accepted remedies, both involving giving the victim a drink. This could be made either by cutting an ox hoof into parings and boiling these with bruised mustard seed in wine and fresh water, or taking freshly drawn and still warm blood from a mallard duck, drying it to powder, then diluting with white wine. Both were quite useless.

The authorities tried to control the spread of the plague by isolating Ashburton totally. All trade ceased; no one was allowed to leave the town and none come in so no one escaped devastating hardship. Gossip said that rates were levied in adjacent districts to help the afflicted villages – a burden that became heavier as the disease spread. Ashburton, Totnes, Buckland and North Bovey were supposed to share £150 a week from the donations. But it made no difference as death ripped out the heart of their community.

In the first outbreak, seven members of the Weeks family died within four months. Philippa found her cousin, the small, ten-year-old Symon, wandering the town hungry, ragged and distraught. She took him in and would look after him for the next five years, for he had no other living relative.

§

She and the boy lived in the cottage alone. Gradually life became easier, as memories of the days when men and women could be well at night but dead by morning, receded along with the stench of death. Once the disease had burnt itself out, wages doubled, for labourers were scarce and their work much in demand.

Philippa gave no further thought to marriage. There was no prospect, no opportunity. She just concentrated on the boy and somehow they survived. Soon Symon was showing real skill as a weaver and when an opportunity came for him to work in Exeter, she urged him to go. He would improve his craft and make a good living, for in a cathedral town the demand for cloth was high. So one day in 1633, she tied his clothes in a bundle, gave him some bread and a hunk of cheese and watched him walk down North Street to take the road to Exeter. She didn't expect to see him again.

She stayed on in the cottage where she had lived all her life. No one laid claim to it and this was a mercy. From time to time she took in a lodger, but what money she earned mostly came from her skills with wool. Every week she went to the top floor of a house in North Street that had been set aside for carding. There she met other women and that was company enough. She had learnt to spin too, a craft in which Ashburton specialised.

Yet it soon became apparent that the wool trade, too, was dying out. The tin industry had already gone. She saw only uncertainty in the future and hers stretched no further than a single day. How, during daylight hours, could she earn enough to eat and so live? Soon, she would be thirty; soon old, likely dead.

Jobs, prosperity, even health for a woman depended on male relations and with Symon Weeks gone from her life, she had none.

There were other problems, too. In a period of increasing political and religious unrest, times were fraught. Some in Ashburton were staunchly Catholic; others strongly Puritanical and the divisions and dissention provoked many arguments and fights. Even the vicar was replaced and some insisted so too should be the King. But such talk was treason. Heaven was the only future Philippa could contemplate and she prayed that on the Day of Judgement she would be found to have been good.

Then one late afternoon in early February, 1634, Symon Weeks re-appeared... and changed her life forever.

§

The knock startled her. She wasn't expecting anyone, so opened the door carefully for it was already dark.

She was both delighted and puzzled to see him there. Delighted because she had been wondering how the boy was getting on, puzzled because he was carrying a large bundle as if going on a long journey.

He brushed the snow from his shoulders and hair before entering. He had grown into a lovely lad, strongly built with sensitive hands. She took his jacket, showed him where to put his bundle and then poured water for him to wash and Ashburton ale to drink. Luckily a neighbour had given her a rabbit and she had two onions, some potatoes and bread.

Without asking, Symon went out to the back and brought in wood to build up the fire. They ate in silence. She could not think what had brought him to Ashburton but would let him tell his tale in his own time.

After their meal was finished he untied his bundle and put into her hands a newly woven kirtle and shawl. She was deeply touched. She had never received a single present from anyone before, except the odd coin or sweetmeat at fair times.

"These are finely done, Symon," she said, "and I think you wove them yourself."

"I did," he replied proudly. "I had good work in Exeter so I made these for you in my spare time."

"I doubt there was much of that," she observed.

"Not too much," he agreed.

Her eyes wandered to the bundle on the floor. He caught the look.

"Life's not too good in Ashburton, I reckon, and not all that much better in Exeter either. The wool trade is dying – so I am leaving."

She was astonished. "What are you saying? Where are you going?"

"I came specially to tell you. If it wasn't for you, I'd have long since been dead. I'm taking a ship from Dartmouth to lands across the seas. The Caribbees, they call them. They're in the west."

His eyes were shining with excitement. "The authorities – merchants in London, so they say – are setting up new colonies and their agents are recruiting hundreds of people. They need blacksmiths, husbandmen, tailors, God knows who else – weavers too. They say there's land and a good life for those prepared to work hard. The local vicars around Exeter have been raising money to help people who are too poor to pay for the passage. But I've saved. I've more than enough."

They said no more that night, nor during the next day. He had business to attend to, he said, to do with travelling to Dartmouth where a group would assemble in the port. So it was not until the next evening, after a simple supper of soup and bread, that she raised the question again.

"Why did you come here?"

"As I said yesterday, you gave me a life. Let me give you one."

He came over to her and took both her hands in his. "There's a new start out there. You lost Jim Gye, but there'll be many chances for marriage. They need women just as badly as weavers and blacksmiths. I know two girls from Exeter who are coming, Sara Coose and Judith Stevens. Why don't you come with us?"

She looked round at the bare, dark room and into a barren, dark future. After those dreadful years she was cautious. So she said she would decide in the morning, but in fact she already had.

She slept little that night. When she finally dropped off she was very restless, anticipation merging with trepidation. Though she could not conceive what awaited her she sensed she might be on the cusp of something tremendous and leave she would.

Chapter Twelve

Plunging into the Future

"Princes and Lords may flourish, or may fade;
A breath can make them, as a breath has made;
But a bold peasantry, their country's pride,
When once destroyed can never be supplied.

§

Oliver Goldsmith, *The Deserted Village*

Two days later she left Ashburton for ever, carrying just her new skirt and shawl, some undergarments and a pewter mug, tied in a bundle of rough cloth. They started at dawn, for they had to walk ten miles to Totnes. Once outside Ashburton they climbed up to the ridge, for the winter had been wet and rain storms on the moor had flooded the shorter, lower road. The River Derte that flowed down to Dartmouth, was gentle and quiet in summer, but in winter the brown stream became a foaming torrent, dangerous to cross and impossible to navigate.

Once on the ridge road to Staverton, they paused. Though Symon looked back towards Ashburton, Philippa didn't even turn her head. A new life was beginning so she would look only forwards – something she would do for the rest of her days. The air was cold, crisp and sunny; and they were lucky for there was no rain. They met only a few people on the ridge – just the odd peddler with a pack animal – for at this time of year there was little movement. But they were still wary: the lanes were narrow, the hedges high, and evil always lurked unseen.

Once off the ridge, they crossed the river over the old bridge at Netherton and just after midday walked into Totnes.

Symon had friends in the town. Another weaver offered them simple lodging and so he left Philippa helping the wife prepare a meal while he went down to the river, to see if there might be an easier way to get to Dartmouth than by foot.

Within an hour he was back, looking mightily pleased with himself. "There's a wherry going down in the morning and the man will take us. We must leave early."

She awoke again at dawn. They splashed water on their faces, gathered their bundles and went down to the jetty. Symon gave the wherryman a coin and with three other travellers they embarked. A northerly wind filled the sail and sped them swiftly southwards.

Gradually the river widened and within an hour Philippa saw the distant landmarks of Dartmouth. The black-bearded, laconic wherryman, who spat into the water at regular intervals, steered over to the west bank at Hardness Point and just before the millpond, brought his boat alongside the old quays. Once tied up, he hurried them ashore.

Philippa disembarked first. As the others were climbing the steps, she looked around in disbelief. She was astonished at the sights. Ship after ship swayed in the Roads; boat after boat – wherries, lighters, sloops – were tied to the quays. The bustling, active town carried a successful air of busy prosperity such as she had never seen before.

During the three days they had to wait, Dartmouth constantly amazed her. She had never seen such a place – full of frenetic activity centred around the New Quay, where splendid new buildings were going up opposite the landing points. The town was a huge port of assembly and an excellent haven for ocean-going vessels.

She was told that apart from overseas trade the principal activity at Dartmouth was the fishery: quantities of salt were fetched from across the Channel at La Rochelle for preserving the local pilchards that were sold on in France and in Spain as well as Devon. The town's fishing industry also supplied the nucleus of the crews which would sail for Newfoundland.

She lost count of ships moving serenely with the tide on their way out to sea, while others inched in, for though the tide might be in their favour, the wind sometimes was not. The noises came clearly over the water – the anchor splashing down, the shouts of the commands as the sails fell. On the streets, the oaths, the curses, the raucous laughter, the blessings of fortune tellers, the pleas of beggars, the hammers of construction and the clutch of unfamiliar words — *Maderas, New Found Land, Finis Terre* — were a constant counterpoint against the noise of fights, arguments and drunken brawls. Yet sometimes there was the odd kindness of strangers and a brief exchange of conversation. Dartmouth was an exotic, exciting, tense place of assembly.

As rapidly as he had in Totnes, Symon found his way around. Now he told her that though their ship, *The Margarrett*, was going first to St Christopher and then on up to the Americas, he was destined for Nevis — a small island just a few miles across the straits, where a new colony had recently been established. Some four score planters were already there, so he'd been told — though he couldn't rightly be sure — and they were calling for skilled people — a weaver, a blacksmith, a tailor and husbandmen. She would go with him, she repeated again and so, without any fuss, Nevis became Philippa's destination, too.

Gradually, the lodging house filled. Then shortly after noon, on the 20th of February, a seaman appeared and began rounding them up. *The Margarrett* would sail on the evening tide, but before they could embark, they had to appear before the Magistrate for certain mandatory ceremonies. He herded the men and women into a small procession that moved along the quayside towards City Hall and got larger as it progressed. The fourteen women had mostly started from the lodging house, but many men, rounded up by God knows what rumour, joined as they went along and by the time they reached City Hall there were sixteen of them. The men eyed the women curiously but they all cast their eyes modestly downwards.

At the entrance to City Hall the agent for the ship-owners demanded payment and in turn, they produced coins. Symon paid for them both.

Then they filed into the Magistrate's Room which reeked of authority. One by one, they were told to speak their name, age, where they had come from and occupation. Their details were painstakingly recorded.

Philippa was called seventh. Before her, five men were summoned; all save one, strong and big. The blacksmith, the seaman, the saylemaker, came from Devon. But the buttonhole maker, who came from London, was small, thin and very pale.

Philippa couldn't help noticing that William Haukins, a glover from Exeter, who Symon knew slightly, was looking intently at Margarett Harwood, from Stokegabriell in Devon. She returned his gaze boldly, but most girls were either so overawed or so apprehensive that all they did was mumble the details demanded and a young girl of sixteen was weeping.

Finally, the Magistrate bustled in. A rotund, pompous little man, cloaked in authority and a chain of office, he flourished both with obvious pride. As he entered, his deputy, James Worthy, who was substituting for Mr Thoroughgood, rose to his feet and bowed obsequiously. All the men repeated the bow; the women bobbed. Then, collectively, they swore the Oath of Allegiance.

There would be many such groups that day. The clerks frantically strove to keep pace with the records – and inevitably made many errors, only some of which were rectified. Before they were ushered out, Magistrate Gournay reminded them of what they had just done. Sworn on the Bible, the Oath of Allegiance affirmed their constant and permanent loyalty to His Majesty, Charles the first, to their country and to their Church. To link with any other sovereign or nation, wherever and for whatever reason, would be treason and for treason they would die. Collectively they nodded or bobbed, though Philippa heard one man growl. Then they picked up their bundles and walked down to the quayside where the boat was waiting to row them out to *The Margarrett*.

Somehow they clambered, or were pulled, or pushed aboard, and their bundles flung up after them. As they came onto the deck they saw that the Master was both laughing and cursing. He turned to his Mate and muttered something. Philippa caught the words 'one for each man'. Generally there were at least five men for every one woman on ships taking these voyages, a ratio that could cause all kinds of problems.

All were taken way down below, into a small, dark, foetid area and the men separated from the women. They were shown the space and the hammocks where, in turn, they would sleep. The young girl of sixteen was still weeping so Philippa tried to comfort her. They heard crashes, clangs, bangs, shouts and finally, the soft rippling of water under the keel, as *The Margarrett* slipped out to sea on the evening tide.

Chapter Thirteen

Following the Fluid Line

"Eyes, gazelle, delicate wanderer,
Drinker of horizon's fluid line."

§

Herbert Spencer, *The Express*

The next three months were a relentless nightmare. When the water was sweet, the sea was rough; by the time the sea was calm, the water was foul. There was none for washing and little for drinking. Within a week everyone and everything stank of vomit, stale air, unwashed bodies and rotten food. The space was so cramped in a ship carrying thirty passengers and nineteen crew that they had to take turns to feed and sleep. Bound tightly by the rituals of the ship – the bells, the changes of the watch, the twice-daily prayers – they survived as best they could.

They were trapped in the Channel for six days, being tossed violently by south-westerly gales. When they turned into Biscay they were held for two further weeks by more gales. They inched, crawled, struggled their way past the most westerly point of Spain and rolled, rocked and corkscrewed down the Iberian coast. Philippa heard one sailor cursing loudly, using the word she had heard in Dartmouth – *Finis Terre*, the end of the Earth.

Though the days grew lighter, the weather did not improve until nearly six weeks out, when the *Isles of Maderas* were way to the east. Now their course changed again. As week followed week, the sun rose higher in the sky and the air felt warm, so in turn, they were allowed on deck during the day. Some sneaked out at night too. The skies were bright blue and soon there was a heat in the air that Philippa had never before felt, even in a Devon summer. But the rocking, corkscrew, tumbling roll of the ship never ceased.

They lost count of the days that for over three long months followed each other relentlessly. They never saw another ship, though as the voyage progressed they saw strange fish that shot up and flew over the waves. One day the Master Mariner harpooned a porpoise in a bloody struggle, and for one glorious meal they ate fresh meat.

Though Symon managed to speak with her from time to time, the girls were kept well apart from the men and Philippa took the sixteen-year-old under her special care. However, it was soon obvious that, segregation notwithstanding, Margarett Harwood was regularly meeting William Haukins. One day she told Philippa that she would not after all be disembarking in St Christopher but would go on with William to the Americas where they would marry.

After three long months, when hopes of the voyage ending had faded to prayers for a miracle, on a day which was hot and humid with the sun high in the sky, they heard a cry from the mast head: 'Land, ahoy!' On the western horizon they saw a low green line, but they did not make for the land. Instead, the ship's course altered and a powerful wind carried them northwest. After a few more days they sailed past the island of Montserrat, leaving it on the leeward side. Then an island came into view that seemed to be just one huge green mountain, with a near perfect peak. This, they were told, was *Navis*.

Making skilful use of the currents, *The Margarrett* skirted this island, too, as the wind – now very powerful – carried them across its south-east point. They then turned and reached across the bay to anchor off St Christopher – a long island of several peaks and valleys all smothered in forests of green. Nevis now lay astern and taking a quick backward glance, Philippa saw white clouds cloaking the peak of the mountain top. Entranced, she watched the swooping, predatory black birds with forked tails and white underbellies, that she would come to know well in future years. Then she turned away for there were sounds that she had not heard for months – shouts of command and an anchor splashing down.

A boat was soon alongside. Though they had embarked months before if not with energy, at least with physical strength, they now fell onto dry land with resigned exhaustion. Whatever lay ahead nothing could be worse than what they had just experienced.

As the weary passengers struggled onto the jetty and retrieved their bundles, a group of men began calling out names. Though no one called for her, amongst the voices she heard a shout:

"Weeks. Symon Weeks."

"Here."

"You're to go straight over."

Chapter Fourteen
A Floating Bulwark

*"Just by it on ye Lee shoar; & Mavis appears ahead of vs, hauinge.
3. or. 4. hills, butt one high aboue ye rest appearinge farr of, like
ye banquettinge house att Whitehall ouer ye other buyldinges. Nott
farr from ye foot of this hill, ther is a hott bath."*

§

The Voyage of Sir Henry Colt,
prefixed by a letter from him to his son George,
dated from his tent at St Christopher's, August 13, 1631.

The shallop skimmed swiftly southeast. The stiff breeze carried them on a fast reach across the stretch of water three-quarters of a league wide separating St Christopher from Nevis. There were six other people on board – the Master, his mate and two men who were escorting two others from *The Margarrett*. There was cargo, too: several barrels, sacks of dried goods and bundles of wooden staves.

Seated on the starboard side Philippa had a good view of the island that would be her home. Her eyes were constantly drawn to the top of the cone-shaped mountain. Clouds clung to its peak, mists swirled on the slopes below. Save only for one long, sandy beach the entire island was a dense green forest.

Neither villages, nor settlements, nor people could be seen, though as they came nearer she spotted a wooden jetty and a red-roofed building. But they went beyond and she thought they would land elsewhere. Then suddenly the Master shouted, the sail dropped, the shallop turned back into the wind and drifted gently alongside. Apart from the long, low building and a few shacks beyond, there was nothing there at all.

Sacks, staves and barrels were unloaded. Her two ship-mates stepped off and were led purposefully away by the other two men but Symon and Philippa were left standing on the jetty. The Master jerked his head towards the building with the red roof, so they walked over.

There was little activity — just two men standing by a horse-drawn wagon and a second horse tied to a post. The tall, fair-haired man was supervising the loading of sacks, some axes and two barrels. The other, small, stocky and swarthy, with a squint in his eye, was clearly his servant.

As Philippa and Symon approached the two men stared. There was no greeting, just an astonished silence. Finally, the fair-haired man spoke.

"Who the devil are you? Where d'you think you're going?"

Symon tugged at his hair. "I'm Symon Weeks, a weaver. I was told I was needed over here."

"Were you indeed? Well, we could do with some decent cloth. And you?" he said, turning to Philippa.

"I'm his cousin. I came with him from England."

"Did you now?" he commented and looked her up and down. He saw a strong, well-built woman, who was filthy and exhausted. She saw a tall man with blond hair and a surprisingly reddish beard, who was gazing at her with an amused look on his face, at once expectant and challenging. Yet far from being disconcerted, she felt a response she had only ever experienced once before — at a wedding fair when a man winked at her from behind a pig's ear.

"And *your* name?"

"Philippa Stephens."

"I am Clement Prentis."

Then he turned away, checked the final loading of the wagon and went inside the building which was obviously a storehouse. The servant waited with head bowed, careful not to look at Philippa at all. She heard voices, then two men came out, had a further brief conversation and both seemed satisfied.

Now Clement Prentis spoke to his servant. "Take this lot back up. I'll be with you before the light fades."

He turned to Symon. "I'll take you to the Governor. He'll know where to place you."

As the servant moved off with the wagon, Symon moved towards Clement Prentis. But Philippa hesitated. He'd said nothing to her.

He smiled and jerked his head. "What are you waiting for?" he asked. "The Governor will marry us."

And that was that.

As Philippa finished her tale, she turned to Roger and smiled. "I was very lucky — very lucky indeed. Clement was a good man. There were nearly one hundred planters on the island. Any one of them could just have taken me."

§

In a reassuring gesture, Clement reached for their bundles and Symon helped rope them on the horse's back. Then he led them inland along a rough track, but after a hundred yards or so, turned right along a path that led through woods, thick with huge trees and luxuriant plants. So dense was the growth they could not see where they were. The air was still, hot and sticky. After another half a mile, Clement turned into a small valley and soon they reached a great pool with clouds of steam rising from the water. Two parallel streams ran on either side of the pool and steam was rising from them too. The two travellers were surprised: they thought they were going to the Governor yet there were no buildings anywhere in sight. But Clement stopped and tied up the horse.

Reaching into a sack, he pulled out a bar of soap and with his belt knife, cut off a piece, handed it to Philippa and pointed to one of the streams.

"You need to wash — everything! You, too!" and led Symon to the other stream.

As they moved away Philippa took a quick glance behind her. It was a great mistake, for she saw three men, totally naked, washing in the stream and a fourth naked man moving towards the pool. Quickly she turned to face the other stream. Hearing voices she walked down to the bank and there she saw two women just as naked about to get in.

She hesitated, instinctive modesty battling with stinking clothes and filthy skin. She compromised by slipping into the water fully dressed and only then did she take off her clothes. As Clement had ordered, she washed everything — body, hair and the garments she had worn constantly for the last three and a half months.

She didn't know how long she remained in the water, but must have spent at least half an hour. The other women were smiling encouragement, eager to talk but she couldn't understand a single word.

Hearing a loud whistle, she climbed out, dried herself roughly and put on clean undergarments. Though her skirt was soaking wet she wore it again. She didn't want to spoil the new one Symon had given her. Then she went to wait by the horse. When the two men appeared Symon looked a new man and was grinning broadly – and so, too, was Clement.

§

As she told Roger the story, she saw that he, too, was grinning.

"They call the valley the Garden of Eden," he observed.

"They did so then," she said.

In days to come she soon relinquished her modesty at the springs, for people always bathed at the pool naked as the day they were born. The miraculous powers of the hot water were legendary and greatly blessed by those who had spent months at sea, or who had been blistered and tormented by the liquid that dripped from the manchineel tree.

Clean and feeling much better, they began climbing through the bush along a rough path that ran parallel with the shore line. The great mountain peak clothed with cloud was now behind them, but in the distance she could see a smaller mountain of a quite different shape. Catching her staring, Clement said, "That's Saddle Hill. I live on the other side."

She could see why it was so called. To the right the hill rose like a pommel, while the other end sloped backward like the rump of a horse.

Finally, the path turned inland and soon they came to a large, wooden house set on the lower slopes of rising land, with a small group of huts to one side. Hearing them approach, three men came around from the back and Clement greeted them.

"Where's the Governor?"

"Inside."

"I have a delivery for him."

"So I see," said one man, eyeing Philippa lasciviously and moving to touch her.

"No. The boy. Get away."

Clement was looking so furious that the man quickly backed off.

The ceremony took all of one minute. The Governor produced a Bible, asked if they took each other to be wedded and then said by virtue of the authority vested in him by King Charles I, they were now man and wife.

Philippa took quick leave of Symon and was told that she would often see him again — and Clement kept his word. By the time they reached his land, higher in the lee of Saddle Hill, it was practically dark. There were just two huts and thoroughly makeshift ones at that. She was given a simple meal of potatoes and water and unfamiliar fruit that she liked well. Clement barked an order and two men took out their belongings from one hut, but left a mat and a hammock behind.

So it was there, high in the hills, thousands of miles away from England, with the music of a vast wind in her ears, that Philippa Prentis spent her first night as a married woman. But her husband left her to sleep.

Chapter Fifteen

Mine Own House

"Daughter am I in my mother's house,
But mistress in my own.
The gates are mine to open,
As the gates are mine to close . . . ."

§

Rudyard Kipling, *Our Lady of the Snows*

Once a week from then on, and just before supper, Roger joined his grandmother on the terrace. The others were content to let them be. The men were anyway relaxing after the day's work while the women were cooking in the kitchen.

Every time she watched the sun sink into the sea, Philippa was perplexed – as she had been from her very first day on Nevis. Everyday the golden globe appeared to rise at the same point in the sky above the mountain, and sink near the same point on the western horizon. Whether rising or setting, in January or June, it never travelled along the diagonal slope as in Devon, but rose or fell almost vertically. Why was it all so different from England?

The absence of a prolonged twilight also puzzled her: whatever the month, why was the length of day almost the same? Other heavenly sights were equally puzzling. The crescent of the new moon did not appear vertically above the western horizon, but lay on its back, waxing upwards from below, not sideways from right to left. Most stars were different too – fine jewels set in a deep velvet blackness, sparkling brilliantly at all times. She could make out one or two familiar constellations, such as the Bear, but others she had never seen before.

She came to cherish those times with her grandson, though his questions could disconcert her. By now he'd caught the knack of smoking, lighting the tobacco quickly with his pipe drawing well and before he spoke, he always saw that Philippa's mug was full and she at ease.

However, his first question that next evening was one that she absolutely would never answer.

"So grandfather left you to sleep that night? But what happened first of all the next morning?"

She closed her eyes and her face remained impassive. He must know perfectly well what happened, for he was a grown man and would likely soon be married. She had no doubt that men talked amongst themselves, but women never discussed such matters with men.

She had been awakened by the movement of Clement's arms lifting her from the hammock and placing her on the mat where he had slept. Still half asleep, she sensed he was wearing just a shirt. By the time he had removed her garments and entered her, she was wide awake.

She was not shocked — after all she was now a married woman. But she was surprised and what caused her surprise was the pleasure she experienced. From that moment she loved him and mutual physical release became a regular part of their joint days.

So what happened that first morning? Her reply was deliberately vague.

"All so different; so very different."

She remembered rising from the mat, rearranging her clothes and looking around. Though the hut was dark she could see that its leafy roof was supported by four wooden posts and that thin wattle acted for walls. Hearing the noise of hammering against the background of a strong wind, she followed Clement outside.

Her husband — *her husband* — she told herself — pointed to a leather bucket of water, so she washed her face. He gave her some cold gruel-like stuff to eat and more fruit — of a bright red, sweet flesh with black pips. The sun was swiftly rising behind Saddle Hill, but after one quick glance, she looked west across acres of intense green that fell rapidly away to a sea of intense blue. As the light got stronger she could make out two ships riding at anchor in Galleons Bay below. Away to her right, she thought she could spot the outline of Red Storehouse on the shoreline and to the northwest, the island of St Christopher was becoming clearer every minute. Already it was another world away and Ashburton a swiftly fading memory.

The two huts in the clearing had been built in front of a group of trees that provided protection from wind and rain. Now a third was being erected.

Six forks of newly cut wood were hammered into the ground and roofed with reeds and leafy branches taken from palm trees and plantain. There were no walls for a few days, but eventually lattice wattle structures were tied around. Everything seemed very fragile.

Immediately below the huts, plants were growing in a large vegetable patch. To the left was a pile of debris, which grew larger as more land was cleared. Eventually, the pile was burnt and the ash scattered on the ground.

§

"Did you recognise any of the plants?" asked Roger.

"Oh, yes. Potatoes, beans, peas and onions. But there were many new ones I had to learn to cook. I was astonished how everything grew quickly. We'd never have got three crops of peas in a single year in Devon. But they needed a deal of weeding."

§

She recognised that from now on weeding would be her responsibility. So she nodded tacit acceptance as Clement led her further down the slope and away to the right where a much bigger area had been cleared. These plants, their cash crops, were quite unfamiliar but she'd be weeding them too. Three men were already at work, clearing away the rocks, stones and weeds, tilling the rich, black earth ready for the seeds.

"Sugar cane, of course," said Roger.

"No, grandson, not then. We didn't grow sugar cane for – let me think now ... oh, some ten years after I arrived."

"So what were those crops?" he asked.

"Well, we had indigo and ginger and we had tobacco."

She remembered standing there that day, looking at the land and resolving that as she was now wife of the master and mistress of the settlement, she had better grow some children quickly while also cherishing the growing crops. Neither task took long.

"Indigo grew fast," she told Roger, "but it was very tricky. Good rains are needed and as you well know, you can never be sure when they will come. Some years there were droughts but in others there was far too much rain – and that was just as bad because indigo plants are easily smothered by the weeds. They could take over in days. So you just planted and weeded and planted and weeded. It never ended. You could never leave a patch fallow as we did in Devon. Tobacco was much easier. You could grow many plants close together on just a small piece of land and the weeds weren't a trouble because tobacco is just as vigorous and grows real tall. But it exhausts the soil so young plants had to be put in fresh earth very often."

She sipped her wine and water. "Looking after tobacco wasn't easy. It takes a heap of skill to get the leaves ready for picking at just the right time. Still tobacco grew better on Saddle Hill than anywhere else on the island."

"So you did well?" said Roger, puffing happily on his pipe.

"We did for a while. Yet some five years after I married, the price fell sharp away. Your grandfather said that for every shilling tobacco fetched ten years before, we were now getting only one penny. Again I never properly understood why. One year the price dropped so low that the planters on St Christopher pulled up the entire crop and swore not to plant until a year and a half had gone by."

"But this can never happen with sugar," Roger said blithely.

"Never say 'never', grandson. It is to call up evil. I don't wish to hear you tempt fate. You cannot foretell what may come to pass. Remember the scourges that regularly afflict us – ants, droughts, hurricanes, fire, mosquitoes, bugs, blights, fevers and plagues."

Though out of respect Roger stayed silent, he was not convinced.

§

By the end of her first morning she had a good idea of what life would be like on Saddle Hill. She thought she counted six indentured servants who touched their forelocks every time Clement came by. There could have been more, there might have been less, but that first day she couldn't distinguish between them. As the day wore on her sense of responsibility increased. Not only was she now a married woman but they had land and servants. Her job was to feed the men, wash the clothes, weed the crops, sustain everyone by providing a good meal at the end of the day *and* remain cheerful and constant throughout.

That evening Clement brought meat.

"I didn't know at the time," she said to Roger, "that it was a large rat, *agouti*. It tasted a bit like the rabbits we'd had in Ashburton. The coneys, *hutia*, that Clement bought in later really were like rabbits. And there were iguanas — lizards — that I'd never seen before."

They ate meat once, sometimes twice a week and she soon learned how best to stew the weird animals. There were wild hogs from the forests, as well as pigeon-like birds and turkeys. Eggs they had often, sometimes from the turtles whose dark yellow flesh tasted real well.

Occasionally there was fish — some very like the mackerel she'd sometimes had in Devon. Yet though she tried to vary the monotony, the men enjoyed potatoes best of all, so soon she was regularly serving sweet potatoes, cassava and plantains.

Suddenly she developed a huge craving for fruit and later wondered whether this had something to do with how quickly she came with child. There was a huge variety — paw-paws, soapberry and guavas, golden apples with sweet flesh, soursop, mangoes and a cherry-like fruit with a big pip in the middle and prickly pears. She liked them all.

But painful experience quickly taught her to avoid the poison apple that looked like the crab apples of Devon. Growing on the manchineel tree the oozing liquid provoked red wheals so intensely irritating that a man could go half mad with the pain.

Every day was much like any other and she fell easily into their unchanging pattern. Each morning she would study the peak of the high mountain which dominated the landscape at their back, to see whether she could guess what weather they might expect. Though she never could, she would always look. Were there gods and spirits moving in the summit's swirling mists? Was the mountain a ladder to God and Heaven?

She believed in God and still prayed to Him. But since there were no churches, no priests and no services until several years after she had first arrived, she said a quiet prayer every morning. She hoped God would protect her not only in the days to come but eventually in the afterlife, too. In her daily prayers, she gave thanks to Him for her new life and the man who now protected her. For the first time in twenty-eight years, her future extended beyond a single day.

The pattern of the weeks, too, was soon indelibly imprinted. They were working hard to eat and to sell any surplus. With the profit from their crops they would hire more servants, who would clear more land. They could then grow more food and sell more crops and over time their acreage expanded hugely.

But every week without exception, they went down to bathe though she was never quite sure on which day,

"All of you?" said Roger, grinning again.

"All of me – us." And whether by the 'all' she referred to their numbers or their nakedness, she did not explain.

"In Ashburton, we took a bath only once a year, after winter had passed. But your grandfather insisted we went to the springs every week. The servants grumbled, but I believe he was wise."

"He was," said Roger, "but the men were lucky to have you, too."

She knew this was so. Clement knew, their servants knew, how fortunate they were to have a healthy, strong woman in their midst, who brought a welcome degree of comfort into their lives.

Philippa soon noticed that her husband stayed well away from island politics and government. He played his role in the island's defence when called on to do so, but rarely went to the harbours at Musquett Bay or Galleons Bay – only to Red Storehouse to pick up supplies. Of course, she never asked him about their isolation: it was not her place. Having heard some of the women at the baths talking of arguments, fights and even court cases, she wondered if the reason lay there. Her husband was content to stay aloof with his wife, and other men knew full well that he was determined to protect his possession. No one bothered her at all and the servants were most respectful. Perhaps they feared his fist, though she never saw him wield it.

Within eight years Clement had built a real house. Even though it was just one room to begin with, and a tall man could only just stand upright inside and for three further three years the cooking area remained outside, they no longer lived in a fragile hut.

"Is this the house?" Roger asked.

"This is it —though we've added to it over time. Somehow your grandfather found proper craftsmen to help – a carpenter and a couple of handymen. Our servants simply didn't have the skills."

"How did he pay them?"

"With sugar, of course."

She remembered the construction well for there were more men to feed. But between weeding and cooking she would often watch. They had first measured out the room, then sunk four upright wooden posts into the ground. These were made from *lignum vitae* – indestructible timber that wouldn't rot or float and was even hard to saw. Once the corner posts were in, cross timbers were set at the top so the four posts were bound to each other. Several sloping beams were next set in place, moving upwards from the cross beams to a common point in the roof and pinned in with wooden pegs. Roughly worked planks provided the walls. To begin with the roof was thatch but as they became wealthier, Clement replaced this with shingles.

Once the house was finished, a stonemason built a covered cistern that stored the rainwater running off the roof. He used smoothly-faced stones stuck together with *tarras* – a waterproof mixture made from mixing a local plant and lime. Neither animals nor debris could spoil the water, for the rounded roof and the stone walls fitted with sweet precision and the cistern was totally enclosed.

A rectangular drip filter and water cooler, ten feet high, came next and this Philippa felt was best of all. There was space underneath for a large jar with handles, that once held oil and came from Spain, she was told. Spain meant nothing to her, but cool fresh water meant everything. A large, hollowed-out stone was placed on top of the rectangle and through its fine pores the water from the cistern slowly filtered into the jar and stayed cool and fresh.

Roger was no fool. This had cost real money. "How could Grandfather have possibly afforded this?" he asked.

"I wondered myself sometimes, but he never told me and it was not my place to question. He did speak sometimes of his family's land in the Fen country. He was a second son, so I'm believing perhaps he sold some of his inheritance. But he said he would never leave Nevis."

"I'm believing that too, now. But if he was a second son, he couldn't have had much of an inheritance. Perhaps one day I'll find out."

"I doubt it, grandson. Just accept how lucky we were."

§

The days slipped into weeks and into a regular pattern of years. December to April were the best months for the winds shifted to the north east and blew straight over the high mountain and the air became cool. But in May and right through to the end of October, the heat and the humidity increased greatly and the air became still and dead.

In those summer months, there were sudden storms of such violence that the very fabric of the island shook. Crops, trees, huts and ships could be battered to pieces. Not long after Philippa had arrived there was a hurricane so huge that several ships went aground in the bay. Their cargoes spilt and the fish were poisoned from the tobacco floating in the water.

But they survived, their settlement flourished, everyone stayed healthy and two months after her marriage she knew she was with child.

"My father, of course," said Roger. "When was he born?"

"No, grandson. Your father, Roger, was our second child. Our first born was baptised Clement, of course. He was two when your father was born. But we lost him a few weeks later, from a fever."

The speed with which the *ague* had struck was devastating — much like the plague at Ashburton. The toddler was well and happy the night before, but by daybreak next morning he was dead. They wrapped the tiny body in white cotton and buried their first son in a patch of land below the settlement. Philippa felt her heart was bleeding with grief, but forced herself to recite what she could remember of the committal prayers as calmly as she could.

Chapter Sixteen

A Dark Dilemma

"Custom reconciles us to everything."

§

Edmund Burke, *On The Sublime And The Beautiful*

The five dry months from January to May brought a break in their evening talks. The sugar harvest was in full spate and as harvest time was crisis time no one had a single free moment. Speed was essential, for cane juice ferments and turns sour within a few hours. Once cut, the cane was rushed to the mill and immediately chopped up, fed into the grinder, then pressed, ground and boiled. Those toiling in the boiling house worked day and night. When one rested, another took his place for they could never stop until the exhausting job was finished.

So Philippa knew that Roger wouldn't be with her again until the end of May at the earliest. She missed their meetings greatly for she took great joy in the young man who would inherit – and extend – the legacy left by Clement. His obvious fascination with her past had helped her recall memories that a busy life had smothered. Now she had a short time to reflect, as she reconciled herself to the dark void of her future.

Sugar had brought them so much wealth, but sugar had also given Philippa first a human dilemma and then great personal sadness. She had been on Nevis for just over ten years when Clement moved out of tobacco, ginger and indigo. He was one of the first to make the switch into sugar and did so some five years before the planting of cane was officially permitted. However, it took a further ten before the whole of Prentis Works was given over to the crop and a mill complex built. Yet even after a decade there were still complaints: sugar brought economic success to Nevis so quickly that officials soon argued – with, Philippa admitted, real justification – that food crops were being dangerously neglected. But no official could fault the owners of Prentis Works as Philippa and the other women were as busy as ever, weeding and growing vegetables.

Nevertheless the family soon had several ten-to-twelve acre fields of cane, and three thousand plants could be set in a single acre. Yet sugar not only required more land than ginger or tobacco before a profitable return appeared, but also more hands. Two men were now needed to work every two acres, rather than one for every five. The work was punishing but the potential rewards were enormous.

Cultivation began in October and went on until January. The servants and the slaves cleared the ground of grass, shrubs and weeds – which they burnt – then prepared the earth. The ground was too rocky for ploughing so had to be hoed by hand. Sometimes the plants were placed in trenches, sometimes just in holes. Several cane tops could be placed in a single hole and lightly covered, but like potatoes had to be regularly earthed-up. The weeds flourished too, of course, so the rows had to be cleared at least three times between planting and harvest.

After fifteen months the fully grown plants were taller than a man and were cut with machetes. New shoots, the *ratoons*, would then spring up from the stumps and these could be harvested in just a further twelve months. This was repeated twice more, but then the ground had to be entirely replanted.

As she sat on the terrace, Philippa could hear the noise of the harvest – the cut canes being carried to the mill by mule and cattle carts, or on the heads of the slaves; random thumps as the bundles were unloaded in high heaps around the mill house were followed by regular thuds as slaves chopped the stalks. The best part of the cane would be fed straight into the grinders, the useless end used as fuel for the boilers.

Years back when Clement had first built a mill complex, he had used wind to power the grinders. The wooden windmill he built was just like those in the Fens, he said. Apart from the fact that the wind was free and required no food, Philippa thought the mill so beautiful. She loved the way the sails could be reefed, tied, or set fully and how easily, by means of a pole directly beneath the vanes, the wooden upper works could be turned to catch the wind. She loved the noise and the hum of the vanes rotating at full speed, turning a shaft that, in turn, rotated three vertical crushers inside the tower. Best of all – so she had decided with a chuckle – the mill was on dry land and neither wind, nor waves, nor swell disturbed it. But one day a furious hurricane completely shattered the building and from then on the family relied on two oxen to turn the shaft by slowly treading on a platform.

Grinding the cane crushed out a sugar solution that flowed along a gutter to the boiling house, to be mixed with lime and heated fiercely until a clear, syrupy juice evaporated. The temperature and humidity were debilitatingly high, for there was no way to cool the sugar house. The cane was boiled and skimmed until it was on the point of crystallising into 'strike'. She did something very similar in her kitchen when making syrup.

The fluid was then ladled into pots with small holes in the bottom and there it would remain until brown crystals of muscovado sugar separated from the molasses – a viscous part which would never crystallise. They ate some of the molasses themselves, exported some and boiled up the rest into second-rate sugar. Other people would distil the molasses into rum, but not the Prentises. After standing for some time in the curing house the purified sugar was finally barrelled into hogsmeads or tierces, and carted down to the port and put on a ship.

Even though the Prentis estate only produced molasses and one grade of sugar, their profits were huge. But sugar production demanded well organised labour – labour so exceedingly hard that many said openly that such work was not suitable for white people.

By now the pattern of Nevis society was one that she was entirely comfortable with for in all respects save one, it could have been transported from Ashburton. It was a patriarchal order, based on the master-servant relationship and supported by the twin pillars of authority and obedience. The family and the social economic unit of the household were one and the same. Anyone who lived in the settlement – not only relatives, but servants too – were all part of the family. The one fact that continued to astonish her was that far from being at the bottom of the heap, she was now near the top!

But sugar swiftly changed this social order for it brought slaves to the island and as the acreage increased, so did their numbers. She remembered how perplexed she was when Clement brought up the first group of six men and two women, each with two children – and they kept on coming. On December 31st 1674, William Phillips bought one man and one woman for seven thousand eight hundred pounds of sugar in weight; on the 10th March 1679 Roger, her son, bought one woman for three thousand four hundred pounds; in 1680 Roger, her grandson, bought one man and a girl for seven thousand eight hundred pounds of sugar.

For a start their names were very odd. The men were called Caesan, Sunday, Fido, Cuffy, Winter, and Goodwill; the women Gracey and Love. The children's names she could hardly pronounce: Mystiaa and Quasheba. She rapidly got used to having the women and children around the house, though they had to work of course and were set to weeding the vegetable patches, washing and cleaning. The field slaves were housed in simple huts on small patches of land way down in the valley. They grew their own food and were given dried fish once a week.

Yet slaves presented Philippa with a real dilemma. She could not fail to see the despair of men and women torn away from homes to which they would never return, to serve out bitter lives of harsh toil under white masters. Those working in the house were far better off than those labouring in the fields. They had food and clothes and their cuts and ailments tended. But she could not decide where they should be placed in the order of God's creation, for she had never even heard of black people before, let alone seen them. Being a strange colour, surely they could not be family? But since they worked and lived within the Prentis settlement, they were.

The dilemma was not hers alone. When the first census was taken, one recorder ignored all the slaves and listed only whites as family. But a second recorder listed all whites and their children, all Negroes and their children, as one single family. No one had any idea who was related to whom, only that the male head of the household was the master of them all.

As the sugar trade developed the number of indentured servants fell sharply, not only because planters now preferred slaves, but because the fate of indentured servants was uncertain. The life of slaves was harsh but, since they were bound for life, ironically they were often better clothed and fed than those bound for just four or five years. The reason was obvious: planters had an economic incentive to look after their slaves but no such imperative existed that protected the wellbeing of indentured servants. When it became widely known in England that fewer than half the indentured servants ever *survived* their time of service, the number willing to come over dropped drastically. So the slave population rapidly increased, and now, in Philippa's old age, the number of whites and blacks on Nevis was equal.

Sugar also brought William Phillips to the estate though he did not come as an indentured servant. One day in January 1661, her son Roger, twenty-two at the time, had brought him up from Charlestown. This stranger was considerably older than Roger but they had struck up a friendship. Phillips was a short man, in his forties, stocky with greying hair, dark eyes and a livid scar across his cheekbone and another along one arm. Yet he had an instantly recognisable strength and competence.

Clement, who was now ageing, was pleased with the man and happily delegated some running of the estate and the supervision of the slaves to Roger and his new friend. One day he told Philippa that it was politics, not poverty that had brought William to the West Indies. A small farmer of some substance in Wiltshire, he had fallen foul of the Protectorate by speaking his mind. Arrested and transported to Barbados, he hated it there – too flat, he said. So one night he fled and found his way to Nevis where he heard there was much work. Unmarried, he lived at the edge of their settlement, worked hard and had something of Clement's quiet aloofness. He did not need the roistering company of other men – possibly for good reason.

Though Philippa tried hard to remember the details, the years following William's arrival were murky and out of focus. Yet she had no difficulty in recalling the 17th May, 1667.

She was about sixty at the time – or so she reckoned. The sugar harvest was over and everyone exhausted. As usual she was up at sunrise and before starting work, glanced across to Nevis Roads, the stretch of water running northwards paralleling the long beach. There she saw the two English frigates patrolling – as they did every day – and providing a welcome reassurance. Clement, she knew, was already at the mill for he and William Phillips were to take several barrels of sugar down to the bay for shipment.

She began her work and all was quiet. But suddenly she heard cannon fire from Saddle Hill. The alarm gun was firing at two-minute intervals. She straightened up and looked across the water. The sea was packed with ships. Some were sailing round the south-western point of the island making for the Roads; others to the northwest were stretched in a line at right angles to the leeward shore of Nevis, protecting the approach to St Christopher and hardly moving at all.

The sound of heavy firing ripped up from the water and soon she smelled the cordite. Three men-of-war were bearing down fast on a larger vessel. She could not really appreciate the manoeuvres but knew that battle had been brutally joined and she was fearful, for clearly the French were attacking yet again.

Within minutes a ship protecting the leeward shore of Nevis blew up in three tremendous explosions. No one on board could possibly have survived and Philippa uttered a brief prayer for their souls. Then fire ships came into view, running before the wind and heading towards the French ships to the south.

Philippa ran up to the house, calling to the men, but they had already left. So she rallied the women and set them collecting up her jewellery, their gold and silver coins and valuable plate which they buried in a previously chosen spot on the land. For the whole of that long morning she and the women worked at tasks as best they could. Then around noon she saw a battered group of vessels slowly trying to beat towards St Christopher. Only then was she certain that the French had been defeated.

She ate a little, then rested in the shade of the house, for the fear, the tension and the physical labour had exhausted her. Around four o'clock in the afternoon she heard agitated voices calling. She came out to see her son Roger supporting William Phillips, who was staggering towards her. His left arm was hanging helplessly and he had a bloody gash on his face. He was distraught, pale and in obvious pain.

She helped get him into the house and lay him on a bed. Only when she had dressed his wounds and placed his arm in a sling, was he able to speak.

"Mistress," he said. "I will protect you." And she knew at once that Clement was dead.

Roger told her what had happened; it had nothing to do with the battle. Coming down the main hill the brakes had failed. The horse was pushed forward by the weight of the barrels, the wagon turned over and Clement's skull was crushed.

This was a common accident. She had always feared the roads on the estate — narrow, unpaved and deeply scarred by ruts. Though on the weekly visits to the hot springs, she went down in a carriage or rode a horse, she much preferred to walk everywhere.

They buried Clement at daybreak next morning and laid him by their first child. Philippa held their two-year-old grandson in her arms. Numb and grief stricken though she was, again she maintained her composure for she was mistress of the estate. She was the first to speak with Captain Berry when he arrived to discuss the Saddle Hill defences. Though finally victorious, the English fleet had sustained great damage, so while his ships were being repaired, the family were ordered to light a bonfire on Saddle Hill if an enemy fleet was sighted. Roger made the arrangements immediately. That evening one of the cane fields caught fire and mistaking the smoke for the warning signal, Berry weighed anchor and sailed out to sea. Roger rode down to the harbour at once and sorted out the misunderstanding.

Within four months Philippa had married William Phillips. Everyone felt this was eminently sensible. As Clement's son was of age, there was no question of the estate passing to her second husband. But a woman needed the status and protection that marriage brought. She and William had known each other for many years; he was now part of the family; the boys and grandchildren liked him well. But no one – not even Philippa – ever dared ask him how he came by those dreadful scars.

Though child bearing had long passed nevertheless together they were able to create something of great value. By ensuring that the land and wealth established by Clement was carefully preserved for his grandchildren, they consolidated a future for the Prentis family.

Chapter Seventeen

Heirs of all Eternity

"I saw Eternity the other night,
Like a great ring of pure and endless light,
All calm, as it was bright;
And round beneath it, Time in hours, days, years,
Driv'n by the spheres
Like a vast shadow mov'd;..."

§

Henry Vaughan, *The World*

When, in August, Roger was free to renew their evening talks, his grandmother noticed that his curiosity about her life was in no way diminished and she increasingly wondered why. Was he seeking to grasp the links between her past and his future, trying to bridge not just the temporal gap between generations but also the cultural one between the two societies that had shaped her?

Still, she welcomed his questions, though sensed he was mighty restless. Just being a successful *estater* on Nevis would not satisfy him.

The summer was intensely hot and the humidity troubled her greatly. By now she was very fragile and the family treated her with great care. Though in the past she had never allowed anyone to fuss over her, now she let them. Roger also noticed that her spoken thoughts arrived at random without logic or reason.

"Do you realise how much sugar changed Nevis?" she asked him one evening.

He'd never even considered that question so could only give a lame, "I don't suppose I do…" and waited.

But Philippa retreated into silence – not through a lapse of memory but a sudden, surprising realisation. Not until eight years after Clement died did she herself realise how much sugar had changed the society — and by then she'd already been on Nevis for forty years.

This new realisation came about indirectly. Symon Weeks had a flourishing weaver's business in a town that bustled with prosperity. But she'd heard that he was ill and wanted to see him. So one day William and Roger drove her down to Jamestown, where she was amazed as on her first day in Dartmouth. Mosquito Bay, just across the straits from St Christopher, was packed — the ships blotting out the horizon. Dozens of boats were lying at anchor waiting for a free berth; others, wanting to leave, were waiting for a favourable wind. There were small, fifteen-ton ketches that roved from island to island on *ad hoc* errands and larger vessels that plied between Nevis and the American ports of Boston and New Haven. There were huge ships that voyaged regularly between Nevis and Bristol, Plymouth and London.

Slipping between past and present, she spoke again to Roger.

"When I saw them I thought of *The Margarrett*. I wonder if William — I forget his other name — and Margaret — I've forgotten hers too — ever got married? Are they still alive?"

Roger could not answer either question.

"I watched your father and William loading our wagons, much as Clement was doing when I first met him. But I had never seen so much: staves, barrels of Madeira wine, dried fish, corn, honey, cases of rose water, cheese. And there were also several horses to go up — and slaves."

She remembered her head spinning with worry. "Your father knew very well what I was thinking. He roared with laughter and insisted we could afford this. But I'm anxious still. It's too costly."

They went to Symon Weeks' house. His wife had died four years before, but two of his children lived with him and three others were on St Christopher. All were doing well. But Symon, too, was now old — sixty-four at least!

"I teased him about his figure. Too large, I said, but a weaver's job is sedentary! Perhaps I shouldn't have mentioned his weight for he was not well. His face was blotched and he breathed with difficulty."

They had travelled to Jamestown via the Atlantic road round the east of Nevis. This was a long enough trip so she had stayed that night with Symon and his children. But when in the morning, Roger and William came for her, Symon was weeping.

"He took my hands in his and spoke his blessing. I never saw him again."

She was just as amazed when they returned along the eastern road between Jamestown and Charlestown, that ran parallel to the seven-mile sandy beach. So many elegantly dressed people were travelling, some in fine wagons, others in gigs, others on horseback with their slaves walking. But what really astonished her was how the whole landscape had changed. When she had first arrived in 1634, the forests stretched down from Nevis Peak all the way to the shoreline. But now, fifty years later, the sugar plantations stretched upwards almost to the very summit of the mountain. The cane overwhelmed the land and immediately she worried about fuel supplies: no trees meant no wood. But she did not mention her concerns to Roger.

"I asked your father to show me Red Storehouse again. It was still there but over-shadowed by so many tall buildings."

"Well, that's not surprising, grandmother," Roger said, "Nevis is now the administrative centre of all the Leeward Islands. Did you see the Governor's new residence? Finer than the first one you saw!"

She had – but she'd also seen numerous active trading posts and shops – with some on the outskirts of town actually being run by Negroes. The overall air of prosperity was unmistakeable. There were rather too many inns and taverns for her taste and this provoked another thought.

"But I suppose that ships' crews and labourers have to have some relaxation. Of course, we went to the springs and I bathed again. Your mother helped me. But I don't often go now – not at all in fact. I miss the water."

"Grandmother, you're tiring yourself. Take some more wine."

She drank a little, but continued speaking. "Did you know that as they laid your grandfather in the earth, I held you in my arms?"

"No," replied Roger quietly. He couldn't have known for he would have been just two years old.

"And here you all are – alive and well and Sarah, Ann and Edward..." Then she fell so quiet that he thought she had fallen asleep.

Actually, she was reflecting yet again. For though she had been speaking about her past, once again she sensed the change in him and knew her instinct was right. The boundaries of their small island were becoming too constricting. One day, some fifty years ago, she had quite unexpectedly imagined new horizons. She had sensed she was on the cusp of something remarkable, but she had no way of knowing what awaited her. Yet, since she was poor with no future, she had eagerly grasped the opportunity offered her by a young orphan she had befriended. However, her grandson's imagination and eagerness for new horizons were entirely self-generated. He was not poor; he did have a future. Yet he was restless, and she was puzzled. Even so, his next words did not surprise her. Everyone had to make their own lives.

"Grandmother, I have decided to go to England one day. I want to see something of the world. I'll visit Ashburton. I'll visit East Anglia too and come back and tell you all about it. But I have to go."

Philippa became very still. Breathing was suddenly difficult and a ghost walked on a grave. But whose? Likely hers. "Perhaps you will, grandson. God protect you if indeed you leave."

There was a call from the house and Roger rose. "That's father. I must speak with him." But before leaving he poured more wine into her pewter mug.

He was gone no more than ten minutes and when he returned she was still sitting quietly in the chair.

"Grandmother," he said, "I've told my father what I want to do and he is perfectly agreeable."

There was no reply.

"Grandmother," he repeated, and touched her gently on the shoulder. The pewter mug slipped to the ground and the wine spilled over his shoes.

§

While her servants washed her body, the men dug a shallow grave next to her husband and their first-born son. They wrapped her in a shroud of white cotton and buried her at daybreak next morning. The area was fenced so no animals would disturb their rest.

So she lay for three days. Then one morning, Matthew Vanhalmael, a close friend of young Roger and some five years older, came up to Prentis Works. He was a Dutchman who had not long been on Nevis. Being an expert on windmills, he was in great demand, especially in the weeks after the harvest – the recognised time for repairs and renovations.

After spending several hours working in the mill house he joined the men on the terrace for wine. He offered his condolences on Philippa's death and volunteered that Jamestown now boasted a fine stone carver, James Stanclift. A year or so back he had sailed from Bristol on the *Nevis Merchant*, and Vanhalmael had arrived on the same vessel.

The next day son and grandson rode down to Jamestown. No marker stone had ever been placed on Prentis Works – only simple wooden crosses – but there was going to be one now.

Stanclift was a real craftsman – quiet and competent. He took them around his yard and showed them various pieces of stone. Marble from England was far too expensive. Philippa would not have approved such extravagance. But a slab from Hurricane Hill suited well, so Stanclift asked what he should carve.

"Her birth date; her age?" he suggested.

They didn't know either.

"Well perhaps it's for the best. The more words, the more it costs and the greater the risk of cracking. The stone is very brittle. We'll make it simple."

They agreed his price and paid him in advance.

Two months later Stanclift sent a message to say that the tablet was ready for collection. He was sorry the job had taken so long, but there had been a hurricane in October that had delayed everything. They were to send down a large wagon, for the stone was heavy.

The next morning the family and servants gathered again at Philippa's grave when her stone was secured in the earth. Since few could read, Roger, her grandson, spoke the words.

Here lyeth the body
of Philippa Prentis
Phillips, the wife of
Clement Prentis and
after his decease
the wife of William Phillips
Departed her Life August the XI,
Anno Domini 1683.

Afterwards Roger left the others and walked up towards Saddle Hill till he reached their highest pond. There he stopped and faced south west, to gaze over the view that his grandmother had seen every day for nearly fifty years.

Everything was very tranquil – just a gentle breeze. But as he stood an osprey flew up and hovered above the pond. Very likely it was Philippa's free spirit returning to the land she had loved.

And as he was alone, he wept.

Chapter Eighteen
Queen of the Caribbees

"Ships that pass in the night, and speak each other in passing;
Only a signal shown and a distant voice in the darkness;
So on the ocean of life we pass and speak one another,
Only a look and a voice; then darkness again and a silence."

§

Henry Wordsworth Longfellow, *Tales of a Wayside Inn: The Theologians Tale.*

In the months following Philippa's death, Matthew Vanhalmael and Roger Prentis became close friends. The Prentises welcomed the young Dutchman into their family and he was grateful, for he had no compatriots on the island. Though some wondered why he had not gone to the Dutch Antilles, given that war with the Dutch was part of Nevis's recent history, they never probed. There was an accepted discretion about people's past – a realisation that for good reasons most preferred to keep such details to themselves.

But Roger often questioned him about Europe and discussed his own urge to travel. Matthew noticed however that though Roger's father would always nod agreement, a caveat invariably followed: the demands of the estate were presently too great; there would be better opportunities later.

The two young men worked hard and roistered hard. Every Saturday they would go down to Bath springs and then onto Charlestown where there was rum in the taverns and prostitutes in the brothels. The streets were packed, lively and ribald; drunkenness pervasive and fights frequent. The Governor had labelled the town a *'sink of debauchery'* yet claimed that, thanks to his efforts, it was now *'as orderly as any port in England'* – a remark that provoked sceptical laughter both from those who knew English ports and those who knew the Governor.

But the two young men were careful. Losing one's virginity was one thing; losing one's temper in a fight, or one's wealth in gambling, was something quite different. Licentiousness had never been a significant trait in the Prentis family and Matthew himself came from Puritanical Dutch stock. Besides there was another strong imperative that regulated their conduct – the demands of sugar. The trade had exploded and the plantations, along with the slave population, had expanded even though people were warning that sugar lands on high elevations were being 'worn to the bone' and were difficult to manure. But few planters up on the mountain took any notice. Since there was more rain higher up on Nevis Peak, the sugar matured first, was processed first and reached the markets first. So they were getting a far better price than those whose plantations were lower down.

"How long can this go on?" asked Matthew one day.

"Are you talking about sugar or slaves?"

They were in the mill house checking the gears, supervising repairs to the sails. The days were hot, heavy and wet for it was the last week of November, 1688.

"You can't separate them."

"I know that," replied Roger, "But quite frankly, I see no end to either. When I was a boy the population of about eight thousand was half white, half black. Now we're well over ten thousand and even though only ten per cent of us are white, I can't see any reason why this prosperity should ever stop."

Matthew was more cautious: "How can you be so sure?"

Roger hesitated and wiped a cloth over a face that was running with sweat. He was remembering his grandmother's words cautioning him not to tempt fate. However, that was over six years before and the economy was booming. Most likely her warnings had come from fear of the unknown – not only his future, but hers too, as she approached her final voyage. But in his heart he knew full well he did her an injustice. Philippa had little fear and much experience. Yet still he repeated to Matthew what he had said to her.

"I think sugar will support us forever. We make the finest in the West Indies. Our yields are two-and-a-half times greater than St Christopher's and the soil's so rich we need no fertilizer."

"It takes all our energy though," observed Matthew.

"True, but we're young. We've got plenty."

The light was fading fast and their pace of work had slowed. With a nod from William Phillips the slaves stopped work and made their way down to their huts.

"Come on, let's go and join my father."

The two men splashed water over their faces and necks, slipped on their shirts and walked up to the house.

The same terrace, the same view, the same wine, the same pewter mug — which Roger now used. He lit his pipe and allowed his thoughts to drift back to Philippa. But then he dragged himself back into the present, for his father was speaking forcefully about disturbing changes in Nevis society and Matthew was nodding with appropriate deference.

"… We might be rich and flourishing. We might be heading the Administrative Council of the Lesser Antilles, but we're actually becoming more and more unstable …"

Roger was shocked. He could not believe what he was hearing. "Surely not, father!"

"It's true. Your grandfather, Clement, saw this coming. Though he always insisted our family stayed well away from political manoeuvrings and disagreements, they still affect us. A few months before he died he told me about the rapid turnover of the white estate owners. As the years have gone by this instability has deepened."

"Why is that, sir?" Matthew asked.

"The reason is obvious, as Clement clearly saw; imprudent plantation management — because of the carelessness of local supervisors combined with the indifference of absentee estate owners. Such attitudes lead to heavy debts and these trigger the sale of the land, either by foreclosure or by purchase. Over the past thirty years, through the very same process, many properties have been amalgamated. So we'll end up with a few rich men owning a vast number of slaves and most of the plantations."

He turned to his son. "Your grandfather insisted we learnt from this. Follow his example, son. Whatever it costs keep Prentis Works in the family."

As Roger nodded agreement he suddenly realised that actually his father was very insecure, uncertain of his own judgement and decisions. This was perhaps not surprising for he'd had a great deal to live up to. Clement had been the rock, the prime mover, whose work and vision had determined the family's success. Philippa's experience of fifty years on the island provided another tower of strength and clearly his father had relied on her a great deal. But so unsettled was Roger by these thoughts that, for the first time he sought reassurance.

"But the sugar will hold for us, won't it?" he asked. He was almost pleading, Matthew felt.

"That's not the point. The only question is who will own the land. Watch Pinney in particular."

"That planters' agent, who appeared on the island about four years ago?" asked Matthew. "He'd been in a rebellion in England, hadn't he?"

"That's the man. He knows what he's about. He's just acquired an eighty-seven acre plantation and six slaves — simply by enforcing a foreclosure. Now I don't hold that against him and I don't mind what he does down below. But I don't want the Pinneys on Saddle Hill. So watch him — and keep the estate together."

"We could always marry into his family," observed Roger blithely — and immediately regretted the remark, for his father looked stern.

"There are plenty of good families up here, son," he growled, "and it's high time you got married."

Roger took a long drink of wine and re-lit his pipe. He was not averse to marriage: he was twenty-four years of age and knew his duty. But here was yet another reason why travel to England would have to wait.

§

Sixteen eighty-nine was a glorious year — at least to begin with. True the threat of war remained, so the brigades continued to drill and maintain the defences, while the ships still crammed the bays at Jamestown and Charlestown. Although the French took the whole of St Christopher in a sudden invasion, this in no way diminished the commercial euphoria. However, it did trigger many requests from the Administrative Council of Nevis for military reinforcements from other islands. Yet for the first time ever the English refused to send any troops.

The reason was simple. In the second half of the year, a series of major epidemics — malaria, dysentery and yellow fever — devastated the island and, for reasons no one could fathom, hit the men hardest. Neither white nor black escaped; half the male population died. Not for the first time the Prentises welcomed their isolation on Saddle Hill and placed strict limits on their own movements. No one went down to Charlestown or Jamestown except for brief visits linked to their sugar interests. The slaves were not allowed to move at all. Of course, all the Prentis men continued to drill with their brigades, but everyone noticed that the numbers able to bear arms were declining rapidly.

Still, as 1689 yielded to the New Year, Matthew and Roger regularly reassured each other. They would survive, for the sugar continued to flourish.

In February 1690, Roger married. He had known his wife since she was a child and regularly smiled at her across the church aisle on Sundays. Of solid stock, she was the second daughter of the Pemberton family who owned a large estate in neighbouring Gingerland, so her dowry was most satisfactory. He teased his father — the alliance of Prentises and Pembertons could now resist any Pinney encroachment!

Matthew was his best man and the couple spent their marriage night in the Prentis family home. Next day they went down to Charlestown for a day's celebration that included the ritual bath. By April she was with child and prayed that a son would appear in December along with the Christmas winds.

§

April 6th 1690 dawned like any other April day. Roger was working on the estate alongside his father and his brother, Edward. William Phillips had risen before daybreak to ride to Charlestown for the weekly business trip. Matthew joined him a few miles along the road and they would return together in the evening.

About five o'clock in the afternoon, so Matthew would recall, everything suddenly fell quiet. They noticed the same uneasy silence up on Prentis Works too. The dogs ceased barking, the donkeys braying and even the wind dropped. Suddenly a loud, rumbling noise, like thunder, was heard from the direction of Nevis Peak. Though there was not a single cloud, the sky darkened, the blasts intensified and deepened. Then suddenly the entire island went into convulsion. Looking north, Roger saw clefts appear in the mountainside and wave upon wave of watery, black liquid poured out, smelling sickeningly offensive – and still the shaking of the earth continued.

They ran up to the house through the tremors. Trees were uprooted and water from the broken cistern was shooting ten feet into the air while other fountains were appearing through the stones in the earth. Though the women were all screaming, crossing themselves and praying, for surely the end of the world had come, the strong house timbers stood well and no one was hurt. So now the men, too, crossed themselves and gave thanks.

When William returned late that night, he said that every single brick and stone building in Charlestown had collapsed. Only the wooden houses remained standing and many people were dead. Matthew did not return for two days and when he did, his face was ashen.

Only after he had taken wine and recovered a little, did he manage to speak at all.

"It's gone. Totally gone."

"What's gone?"

"Jamestown. Completely destroyed. Only a few people could have survived."

"It cannot be."

"It is so. I got as close as I dared. I met a small group of people surrounding a wounded, battered man clinging to a priest. He would not let go. He was well nigh hysterical, screaming and praying for salvation. When the quake struck he had run inland, but after the convulsion stopped he returned to the shore. He said the sea had gone so far out – almost to St Christopher – that there were big fish gasping on the sand. Then suddenly huge waves came smashing in. The first was the greatest and finished off what the quake had begun. He said one end of the town had dropped into the earth. I don't understand what he meant … but most everyone has gone."

The Weeks family; James Stanclift, the stone carver. It was not possible, Roger thought.

Three months later two thousand English soldiers massed on Nevis, most coming from Barbados. Though the epidemics had pretty much burnt out, the disruption at the north end of the island was still appalling and the strain placed on the island's resources – whether water, food or shelter – immense.

On the 9th July, the English troops invaded St Christopher and to great rejoicing on Nevis, the French surrendered. With English soldiers just across the straits and the harbour of Jamestown no longer offering shelter and facilities, how could the French ever be a threat again?

The worst seemed over. Sugar production shot up and within four years the island was producing twenty percent of the Empire's entire production. Since the merchants in London kept the prices artificially high they were many complaints from the buyers – but none at all from the planters on Nevis.

The harvests on Prentis Works were superb and the house that Clement built expanded yet again. The family could afford tea sets, porcelain and pearl ware, butter, candles and cheese. They bought jewellery and linen for their women, as well as rose water from Bermuda and Bellarmine pottery from Germany. The men drank 'Maderas' wine from Madeira, and 'syder' from Bristol, and rode horses from Boston. A splendid leather chair from Prussia was presented to the elder Roger, as head of the family. Best of all there was no worry that anyone could buy the estate, for they had no mortgage, no debts, worked harder than ever, saved well, bought more slaves and extended their land.

The ospreys, too, still came to the pond below Saddle Hill and every time he was up there, Roger thought how pleased his grandmother would have been. Yet her words often returned to haunt him.

§

When, seventeen years later, in 1707, Roger Prentis finally left for England, he was actually most reluctant to leave. The day before he sailed he spent many hours in the best parlour with Matthew, sorting out the pleas, the depositions and legal documents prepared for the Lord Commissioners of Trade & Plantations in London. The two men, now in their forties, were both grey and beginning to age.

Roger's father was in his late sixties. He was frail and quiet, for the previous twelve months had taken yet another terrible toll. Though there were wives, children and grandchildren aplenty, most of Prentis Works lay in ruins – as indeed did most of Nevis.

The door opened and Roger's younger brother Edward came in and helped himself to some wine. He carried another bundle.

"All the signatures are there and properly witnessed," he said, "I'm truly glad you are going, brother. I don't trust the agents either here or in London."

"If you hadn't been here to take care of the family, I wouldn't be going," retorted Roger as he checked the pages and placed the folders in a leather bag which would never leave his side.

Edward's eldest son — another Edward — came in and greeted first his grandfather, then his uncle. He was a comely lad, fair-haired like his great-grandfather, Clement. Matthew watched old Roger greet and speak with his sons and saw the pain flickering in his eyes — a pain they all shared. But Matthew knew, too, that the old man, broken by the past year, had had a change of heart and had urged — indeed commanded — his son to go to London.

Roger had the greatest affection for his brothers, who had always worked hard alongside him. Edward in particular, had been responsible for maintaining the defences above the house on Saddle Hill and had regularly canvassed support for rebuilding the forts and constantly manning them — an attitude that had earned him the undying friendship of Governor John Johnson. Unlike most of the administration, who were smooth lawyers or foppish clerks, the Governor was just a 'bold soldier' and though he could neither read nor write, thoroughly effective.

Yet if Prentis Works and the whole of Nevis now lay in ruins it was neither the fault of men like Edward nor that of the Governor. Restoring the island's economy would be the hardest task they would ever have to face and Roger fervently wanted to remain with them while they tried. But he had no choice: someone had to go to London.

Over and over, the two friends Roger and Matthew had talked about what had happened. Worse than the epidemics, worse than the earthquake, how could the administration have been so incompetent and how could the French have been so clever? Most interesting of all they agreed, how could so many of the slaves on Nevis have been so loyal?

The first French attack had taken place in the last week of February 1706, with an invading force of a massive one thousand troops. The earthquake damage to the area around Jamestown notwithstanding, they had still tried to get ashore at Cade's Bay, just a short distance across the straits from St Christopher.

But God had helped the English with bad weather and accurate fire from the shore batteries. The determined strength of the Nevis militia – of over four hundred men, helped by one hundred and twenty-five regulars from Antigua – repelled a landing.

The French tried for five days and then, in disgust, invaded St Christopher instead. Meeting practically no opposition they plundered the island. Everyone believed that they would attack Nevis again, so the militia was ready and waiting at the north of the island. But in March 1706, Governor Johnson had to leave for Antigua and a hundred and twenty-five regulars went with him.

Whenever Matthew and Roger discussed what happened next, incompetence of the administration lasted for about three glasses of wine, while the devious brilliance of the French commander, Pierre LeMoyne d'Iberville, was introduced around the sixth.

On 13th May, though the family on Saddle Hill had noticed six French vessels anchored off the south end of the island, they thought nothing of it. For the larger part of the French fleet – some thirty-six ships that had sailed up from Martinique – had been seen in the Atlantic to the east. They had sailed round the north end of the island to anchor once again near Paradise Beach and when, at daybreak, the French delivered a thunderous bombardment, the Nevis militia returned fire and waited for the land attack.

However, the enemy finally came in from the south west, for, way out in the bay, nine hundred French troops had been hidden on six ships. Meeting no opposition at all, they landed and started their march towards Charlestown.

They were not spotted until they were at Fort Charles. The guns were brought to bear and on a hill above Bath Plain, a mere handful of Nevis militia attacked the French column. But Fort Charles had only fifteen defenders under the command of Major Parris, who had to protect both the Fort and the twenty-two merchant ships in the harbour. They held out until three o'clock the next day and when they finally surrendered were accorded full honours by the French for their bravery. But once the Fort had fallen the merchant ships in the harbour were looted and burnt. The enemy then moved on to Charlestown where there was no resistance at all. The town was fired, the records pulled out of the Court House and burned, then the Court House razed. By the afternoon amidst the mass of smoke and flame the French flag could be seen flying on two forts.

As the action began, Roger and Edward quickly supervised the burying of the family jewels and treasure. The bulk of the slaves were sent to their huts in the valley way down below Saddle Hill, though a few stayed with the family. Some had already disappeared up the mountain to fight the French and would hold out for fourteen days. A few hours later the remnants of the Nevis militia marched up the road between Saddle Hill and Nevis Peak to a redoubt some twelve hundred feet high on the mountain, where they were met by other planters who had taken refuge up there – Edward amongst them.

Edward was later to report a heated discussion between the militia who were prepared to fight to the end, and the citizens – who insisted on surrendering – arguing that only by adopting this course could anything of the island be saved. They prevailed. But Matthew and Roger believed that nothing would have made any difference, for from the outset the French intended to take fearsome revenge for past defeats. Moreover, the French commander was so contemptuous of the surrender without a fight that, with unrestrained zest, he exacted a terrible price.

All too soon the French arrived at Prentis Works. The sugar mills were stripped of machinery, the mill house was set alight, as were some of the slaves' quarters. Luckily, the soldiers didn't bother to go right down the hill.

Though scattered remnants continued to hold out on the great mountain, within fourteen days Nevis had been reduced to a ruin. Over three thousand slaves were taken on board the French ships; many leading Nevis planters, Edward included, were rounded up and threatened with death if they did not turn over another twelve hundred slaves. Four planters were taken hostage and transported to Martinique. Finally after eighteen days the French left.

The devastation was unbelievable and within a month the population was starving. Sugar production plummeted to a mere five hundred tons and the loss to Nevis's economy was estimated at one million pounds. Roger's father would never recover from the shock, and this time even Roger came to believe that sugar could not be their salvation. Within weeks the planters organised a petition to the English Parliament asking for a loan to help them restore the economy and this was eventually approved. When the Nevis residents were told to submit lists of their losses, the Prentises – both the men and the women – all put in claims. The lists had to be prepared in precise detail and the agents submitting them to the Commissioners in London were warned that the process could take as long as four years. In the event it took over twelve.

Some argued — erroneously as it turned out — that matters would be expedited if personal representation were made in London rather than the papers passing through an agent in Nevis and a lawyer in England. In the light of this, Roger's father told his son to go to London. Roger felt there was no way he could refuse, for the old man, now nearing the end of his life, knew that the estate was in ruins and the legacy of Philippa and Clement, shattered. This was not the way Roger had planned to visit England, but go he must.

Matthew helped him organise his papers and his luggage. They also managed to put some sugar into casks and get them on board the *Martha*. As the ship slipped anchor in the autumn of 1707 and Roger saw the mountain recede, he thought again of his grandmother's final words: "God be with you if you go."

Matthew watched the *Martha* set into the bay, then rode slowly back up to Saddle Hill.

§

Seven years later on 22nd December 1713, Matthew himself was in London. Now a successful merchant in his own right, he had much personal business to conduct in town. He also had one particular affair that he urgently needed to complete. The compensation claims were still moving forward, though at glacial speed. The Commissioners were now insisting that anyone making claims because of the French destruction seven years ago had to swear on oath that they were re-settling the plantations, were residing on the estates, and would manure, replant and manage the land. That was one particular piece of evidence he was happy to provide. But he had another.

He was shown into the Commissioner's office in the Strand, where he met a man who had commercial interests in Holland as well as the Caribbean. Since Matthew had been highly recommended, the Commissioner was willing to receive him.

He listened carefully to Matthew's story and while taking him downstairs to another room, explained why he was in a position to help. The Council of Trade & Foreign Plantations had been set up by the Crown in 1696 and acted under the Great Seal. Mostly the staff was unsalaried – *ex officio* commissioners who didn't attend the Board regularly and were not even expected to do so. However, a few were paid – he was one – and it was to them that the real business was entrusted. Thus he was perfectly confident in what he was about to do and assured Matthew that appropriate action would be taken.

He asked the Clerk to produce the claims of Edward, Sarah, Edward and Roger Prentis. The two Edwards were listed as Proprietors of Plantations whereas Sarah and Roger were listed as inhabitants and were only claiming for losses relating to domestic dwellings. The Prentises had appointed Messrs Joseph and Danile Alpens, merchants of the City of London to be their attorneys. Matthew was now told to sit down and dictate his testimony. Slowly, with heavy heart, Matthew did just that. When he had signed his statement, the Clerk pinned it to the back of Roger Prentis's petition.

*"These are to certify to the Right Honourable Lord Commissioners of Trade and Plantations or whom else it may concern that I Matthew Vanhalmael of the Island of Nevis was very well acquainted with **Roger Prentis** of Nevis, **Planter** returned as a joint sufferer by the French Invasion of that Island in 1705-6 with Austin Brown &c and that the said **Roger Prentis** went on a voyage from Nevis bound **for London about the year 1707 or 1708**, in the ship called the **Martha**, John Mather, Commander of London &c and that the said **Prentis** or ship **Martha** has not since that time been heard of at Nevis but is generally believed by all people to be lost & **perished** with all the People on Board her. Witness my hand . . ."*

Part Three

Time like an ever rolling stream
Bears all its sons away;
They fly forgotten as a dream
Dies at the opening day.

§

Isaac Watts.

Chapter Nineteen

The Logic of Random Facts

"People and their landscapes change from layer to layer, but they are moulded by previous layers and they remain in touch with them."

§

The Long Recessional, David Gilmour

Though the precise details of Roger's fate remain unknown, some possible clues can be found in a letter written on 8th October 1706, by Daniel Parker of Antigua. He was asking the Lords Commissioners for Trade & Plantations for more help because the most devastating hurricane ever recorded had struck. Though it centred over Nevis, even houses in the nearby islands were totally destroyed. One ship went aground in the harbour at St Christopher; *The Child's Play* was sunk though the crew was saved; *The Winchelsea* had been spotted off shore that evening but was never seen again. Roger's ship might have been at sea somewhere between Nevis and Antigua or even further out. But the date can be easily reconciled with the sworn testimony of Mathew Vanhalmael about Roger's disappearance.

Vanhalmael's crucial evidence was discovered through focussed brilliance by Peter Robinson. While I was seeking Philippa in Nevis and Ashburton, he was ferreting in the National Archives at Kew, and came up with two remarkable discoveries.

I had first met Peter some three years before while instigating a research project on the history of Alfriston where I live, a very old village that in 2006 celebrated the 600th anniversary of the granting of its Market Charter. I contacted the History Department of the University of Sussex, seeking a postgraduate student who would be willing to take on some research, and in this way met Peter Robinson. Bespectacled and modest, he combines the tenacity of a Jack Russell terrier with great historical sensitivity, especially for lives in past times. For him — as for me — history is not a procession of facts so much as the story of people. Since he is a purist about facts, his accuracy is superb. He has two other remarkable traits, however, which compliment my ambitions: he likes to contemplate a larger canvas and is not afraid to publish, happily absorbing any criticism that might follow. Some academics are just downright cowards on this point.

So impressed was I with this young man — some 57 years younger than myself — that I invited him to work with me as researcher and co-author on another book. We have since published two more together and never for one instant have I regretted my decision. I often say that if I was a truffle hunter in Italy and he was my ferreting companion, he would have been stolen long ago.

He rapidly became totally fascinated by the mystery of Philippa and eager to trace the Prentis family down the generations. This meant hours searching the records in his familiar hunting ground.

Peter could walk to the National Archives in Kew blindfolded. He swears he can spot every professional historian as they emerge from Kew station, not only from their bustling gait, indefatigable eagerness and coffee house attire, but because they move with the inexorable intensity of migrating animals.

Yet the buildings whose archives would reveal more of the Prentises' secrets, could not be in greater contrast to those of the charming Nelson museum on Nevis. The imaginatively designed complex of glass and concrete seems to float in space like the Starship Enterprise and the security is fierce. All that can be taken in is a pencil, though a laptop is permitted but only if in a transparent plastic case. Numerous security staff in bright blue blazers, with serious expressions bordering on self-importance, supervise the detector machines primed to monitor document theft. All readers' cards must be swiped at several bar code machines; satisfactory answers must be given to many and varied questions and impatience must be ruthlessly stifled.

In the Map Room, kindly staff, having confirmed requested file references, order the documents on the computer and warn of a forty-minute wait until the boxes arrive. But once called, the researcher moves through another pair of sliding doors to the document delivery counter and working tables. Here Peter would spend three solid weeks following up the tale of the Prentises.

Yet his first exciting discovery – that Roger had been lost at sea – did not just appear. He had many formal documents to wade through and numerous confirmed compensation claims. But as is typical of all bureaucracies, the decisions took forever and when money was finally paid out each planter got only twenty-five per cent of the sum claimed. While Peter quickly turned up the four separate claims made by Sarah, Roger, Edward and Ann Prentis, he had the sense to examine both sides of every single piece of parchment and there he discovered a small thin slip of paper pinned onto the back of Roger Prentis's formal claim. It was the sworn testimony of Matthew Vanhalmael – that from the day Roger had sailed from Nevis he had never been heard of again.

Against a wider canvas, however, Peter's second find is possibly even more significant, for it sheds important light not only on the history of the island, but on the whole picture of trading in the Caribbean during Philippa's last years, when the sugar economy was at its peak.

The circumstances of his discovery are repeated over and over in archives and museums throughout the world. Some documents, whether donated or collected, that no one quite knows where to classify, are frequently placed into a box and labelled 'Miscellaneous' – a convenient, concertina category. Since the term reveals absolutely nothing, as the years pass the records may be first ignored, then forgotten. However, any researcher lucky enough to be handed a box labelled *Miscellaneous*, would be well advised to study the contents carefully.

To say that Peter was gob-smacked when he examined the file, would be an understatement. The staff at the National Archives too, were astonished because they thought that these particular records had been irretrievably lost and some admit that they never knew they existed. What was now under Peter's meticulous gaze was a set of shipping records, covering nearly fifty years, that listed every single ship arriving in, or leaving Nevis from 1680 to 1729. The detail was prodigious; the information staggeringly comprehensive – ranging from where the ship came from, or was going to – whether London, Bristol, Madeira, Bermuda, Boston, New Haven, Gambia or other places in West Africa – to names of Masters and itemised cargo lists.

The following five examples from the hundreds recorded, give a unique insight into life on Nevis during that half a century and the pattern of trade across the continents.

June 17th 1686, in the ship Friends Adventure of London, Master Robert Deane from Guinee, 125 negroes, 1500 lbs Elifents tooth, parcel of beades, parcel of copper barrs, parcel of Ieron knifes, a parcel of lapsales and neckances, '68 men Rebells' being brought to Nevis in the Owner's, Endeavour, from Bristol 17th March 1685/6.

After the failed Monmouth Rebellion, these sixty-eight *Rebells* had been sentenced by the notorious Judge Jeffreys to permanent servitude and exile on Nevis.

September 10, 1684, in the Ship Endeavor of London Stephen Matthews Commander from thence. One box of dry goods, 40 bundles staves, 7000 hoops, 1400 [*] [****] peuter, 3000 wrought iron, 7 [*] haberdasher ware, 30 grosse of corke, 1 box of perriwiggs, 1 chest of dry goods, 2 trunks, 12 reams paper, 5 chests of apothecary's ware, 2000 barrel hoops, 140 bundles of old packt staves, 11 hangers wine, 2 dozen and 10 hatts, 1 small cask wine, ½ a hundred wraight iron, 18 [*] Norwich stuffe, 100 [*] soap, a parcell upholster ware, 6 paires shoos, 1300 [*] wrought iron.

October 11ᵗʰ in the Sloop Sea flower of Bermodas George [******] Commander from thence 3 barrells of pork, 72 barrells of beefe, 44 tubbs of butter, 5 chaires, a parcell of wooden ware, 4 barrells of [***] oyle, 2 nests of tubbs & 2 of pailes, [***] runlet of honey & 3 cases of Rose water.

October 28ᵗʰ in the Ship Batchelour of Boston Arthur Hody Commander from thence 40000 hogshead staves, 6000 pipe staves, 40 hogsheads of packt staves, 6 hogsheads fish, 11 barrells mackrell, 4 hogsheads bread, 2 barrells of floure, 1 barrell of nailes, 11 horses & mares, 4000 foot of board, 10 hogsheads corne, 1 hogshead pease, 40 kentells of fish, 2 barrells of oyle, 1 barrell of onions, [***] sope, 2 [***] stuff.

In the Ketch [******] of Boston Deliverance Parkman Commander from Salem in New England. 100 hogsheads & other small cask of fish, 5000 staves, 4000 foot of boards, 6000 shingles, 9 horses, 4 barrells oyle, 4 barrells cramberries, 14 barrells [***]

We plan to analyse and publish these records in due course.

§

Tracing the story of the Prentises through the next one hundred and twenty years proved equally illuminating. We quickly concluded that Roger did leave children because for years and years the same names keep recurring as the family continued to work their land on Saddle Hill.

Shortly after the French invasion in 1706, the Nevis legislators decided that they needed a reliable means of signalling when an enemy was sighted. However while the legislators insisted that such defence was urgent, they didn't get around to the task for further twenty-nine years. Eventually a fortress was built one thousand feet up on the south side of Saddle Hill and the local landowners were responsible for maintaining and firing the alarm guns. Designed by the Royal Engineers, the stones were huge. The walls ran for sixteen hundred feet and in some sections were as tall as thirty feet.

The Council of Assembly records show that on the 11th November 1735, Edward Prentis, Philippa's great grandson, offered forty-eight Negro working days for the construction. But six years later, in 1741, he asked the Council to excuse his Negroes from any further work and also exempt him from tax, for much damage had been done to his land and a huge volume of water extracted from his cistern and private ponds. He also claimed that he had supplied a great deal of *tarras* for the construction — a rare and expensive clay-type material that was highly prized, since it formed an effective waterproof plaster for the walls. The whole exercise had cost him a great deal and apparently the legislators agreed to reimburse him.

Heaps of other random facts about the Prentises were also buried in the records. The family were never extensive landowners, but neither were they small time operators. They were recognised as successful planters with cohorts of slaves; if you owned just fifty you were considered well off and Peter unearthed details of the slaves purchased by Philippa's sons and grandsons.

For example, on 10th March 1679, when *The Charles* — Captain Joseph Andrews — brought in one hundred and sixty-eight negroes, Roger Prentis bought a woman for 3,000 pounds of sugar. When *The Margaret & Mary* — Captain John Cropale — that had sailed from London to West Africa, arrived in St Christopher in 1680 with one hundred and sixty-three negroes aboard, Roger bought one man and one girl for 7,800 pounds of sugar.

As we were pursuing all lines of enquiry other evidence about the family's activities on Prentis Works came in from another direction. David Rollinson and Vince Hubbard had both participated in a *Time Team* programme on Nevis, broadcast in the UK on Channel 4 television and presented by Tony Robinson. This covered excavations on a sugar plantation just inland from the Four Seasons Hotel. But because the land near Saddle Hill was positively virginal in comparison, David and Vince were far more excited about the excavations that an American archaeologist, Dr Marco Meniketti had conducted over three consecutive summers, on a site identified on an old map as *Prenlis*. His team had worked in an area just below Roland Archibald's house where we think Philippa may have been buried.

The excavations took place during July and August when Nevis is hot, humid and at risk from hurricanes. Since the site was quite undeveloped – no buildings, no roads – the paths that they had hacked out to the site were completely overgrown by the next season and the job held up until they had cut through again. In spite of the obstacles, work went well and by now they have mapped mill structures near a house foundation.

So of course I rang Marco and in the course of a long conversation asked if there was evidence that a house and mill might have been in use on *Prenlis* in Philippa's time. His reply was most satisfactory:

'I have little doubt the works and estate we worked on were in operation during the early 1700s. As for the late 1600s the evidence is less certain ... but not out of the question. Based on a few ceramic artefacts and some construction details of the mill complex, I believe the site was being used by the 1680s. However, most of the early period would have been obscured by later occupation ... But pipe bowls and stems, and a few isolated items all have date ranges that extend back to the 1650s. Someone was doing something in the area before 1700 without doubt.

I should point out that we recovered a significant amount of porcelain and pearlware - mostly tea sets, as well as crystal and cut glass decanter fragments. Although not at the high end of the plantocracy, these folks were living reasonably well, or at least showing off.'

Several elements pleased me. Recalling my earlier visit to the tomb with Brett Wilson – when David had found pipe bowls, stems and an item of pottery dating back into the 1650s – it was most gratifying that Marco had found artefacts within the same date range. Secondly, the presence of other items, including construction details of the mill complex, reinforced no fewer than three of my own previous conclusions: firstly, by the time Philippa died her family was flourishing and she would have known it; secondly, at the time of French invasion in 1706 they were doing well enough for their losses to be significant.

Yet, my final conclusion was rueful. The years since Philippa's death had been so disastrous that I was truly glad she had died when her family's success would have been plain for all to see – a flourishing estate with children and grandchildren obviously carrying on the legacy she had established with Clement. Had she lived longer she might have concluded that everything they had built together had been irretrievably destroyed – whether by earthquake or disease or war or tragic death. And so I wondered: had she known those facts, could she have borne the pain when she was, anyway, close to death?

But, however devastating all those events were, once again Nevis picked up rapidly, so by 1729, when the shipping records end, the island's economy was buoyant once more. The plantations had recovered well and through the rest of the eighteenth century life was easy – apart, of course, from the life experienced by the slaves.

But actually, this was the beginning of the end.

Society would change dramatically in the hundred years following Philippa's death. As Karen Fog Olwig points out, the smaller farm units, which had characterised early colonial society on Nevis, gave way to a large sugar plantations with absent owners. There was a massive shift in population too, as the proportion of black slaves eventually predominated. At the same time, the paternalistic attitude shown earlier by heads of families, also shifted and now plantation owners would never have shared any of Philippa's earlier dilemmas about how to treat slaves. Olwig sums up this change in a felicitous phrase: '*dependants (were now) regarded as necessary stock on the plantation rather than members of the family*'. So while James Rymer – a surgeon who came to Nevis in the 1770s for a visit of several months – might have described the island as '*a patchwork of sugar plantations bordered by trees and bushes*' which he found '*quite enchanting*', the reality was different. With few exceptions the prime objective for overseers and managers was to show a profit first for themselves and then for the absentee owner.

By now, the lifestyle of the wealthy planters – spacious residences, a luxurious way of life and much entertaining – mirrored that of the English gentry back home. So when Horatio Nelson and the Prince of Wales turned up they found a flourishing, self-satisfied society. But in truth the peak of economic success had been reached some fifty years before. One reason why the sugar cane industry on Nevis had been so successful had been the superb quality of the volcanic soil. For decades the planters had not had to bother with fertilizer and plantations extended further and further up the mountainsides. But the time came when the soil was totally exhausted and then the peak of sugar production passed to St Kitts, Antigua and Barbados. There was no way that the island's earlier economic success could last forever and if one wishes to highlight a single fatal blow, it was once again the activities of the French. Ironically, this time it was not by force of arms.

As Napoleon soon realised, the cost of protecting French islands and supporting a sugar industry thousands of miles away was excessive. He was fighting too many battles on too many different fronts. So he offered a cash prize for the first person to crystallise sugar from any plant which grew easily in Europe. A German won the prize by extracting sugar from sugar beet plants. From then on, the price of sugar fell sharply and continued to do so for a further fifty years. The final, fatal blow came soon after with the Abolition of Slavery and the consequence for Nevis is again documented in extensive records in the National Archives.

Though the British government theoretically stopped the slave trade in 1807, they decided to phase in emancipation gradually and plantation owners were allowed to hold slaves for the next twenty-seven years – an enormous length of time. But in 1834 all slaves had to be freed and the owners would be eventually compensated.

One reason why documents exist in the National Archive in such quantity is because many owners cheated. They would claim compensation for certain named slaves, then alter the record for supposedly different ones, but actually claim the same ones twice, sometimes three times over. So the Tri-Annual lists of 1817 were bought in to stop the racket. Every owner had to list the name, age, sex and place of birth of every single slave they owned – not just once, but every three years until 1834 and final freedom. Only then would compensation be considered. The scribes, bureaucrats and lawyers were kept busy for years.

Eight thousand eight hundred and fifteen slaves were freed on Nevis and the total compensation paid was one hundred and fifty-one thousand and six pounds – about fifty million in today's money. The National Archive records show who amongst Philippa's descendants received compensation and the amount they were given.

The documents come to the researcher in a large, book-shaped cardboard box, bound with strong string. Inside is an enormous, extremely heavy, leather tome, flaky and rusty in colour. On some pages the red wax seals are still intact and though the paper is yellow, luckily the ink is bright. In every case, each claim was meticulously written in the same distinctive hand with the same phraseology repeated over and over.

Shortly after Philippa's death, the family had married into a famous and wealthy Nevis family, the Haddocks, and first up in the records was Laurence Haddock-Prentis who regularly submitted claims for he had many slaves. Four lists were submitted by Edward Prentis – a likely great, great, great grandson of Philippa. He submitted one in 1817, two in 1825 and one in 1828, though on the latter he is recorded as *Edward Prentis deceased*, and Laurence Prentis was his executor.

Interestingly Edward did not sign his name on any of the claims he submitted, but just made his mark. He could have broken his arm at just around that time, though it would surely have healed between 1817 and 1828! Or he could have been illiterate, though this is unlikely in a wealthy family. However, there is another possibility. By then some planters had married their slaves. Others had children by them outside marriage and in most cases the offspring were taken into the family. Though mulatto boys especially were given an education, some were not, and it is possible that Edward came into this category. In the event Edward got no compensation at all and it is interesting to ask why. If indeed he was an illiterate mulatto, maybe the bureaucrats in London dismissed his claim as invalid, arguing that there was no way someone of his status could possibly be an acknowledged planter.

But the best discovery of all came from eight original returns all submitted by one Clement Prentis. His first claim, signed with just a squiggle and dated 14th July 1817 (**T71/364**), lists him as Clement Prentis, with five slaves. However, in his next three returns – 23rd February 1828 (**T71/367**), 14th February 1831 and 10th January 1834 – he is Clement Philip Prentis. His final claim, submitted as Clement P Prentis on 1st August 1834 (Claim # 54 **T71/751**), values his slaves at £247 sterling, but in these the signature is not at all clear.

However, I didn't worry too much about his writing for I was ecstatic. By the time I finally read those claims, I had entirely given up hope of finding Clement's name anywhere. Now, finally, I saw solid documentary evidence of his existence. Even after nearly two centuries, descendants had been named after him.

Clement would receive the largest compensation – £98.10s.6d. On 15th February 1836, William Prentis received £39.17s.9d. and Laurence £88.11s.1d. To appreciate the true value, these sums should be multiplied by around 300%.

Nevertheless, at the time many considered these sums to be totally inadequate, for Abolition led to the complete collapse of the island's economy in the second half of the nineteenth century. Ironically, this also indirectly led to the ultimate discovery of Philippa's marker tablet in the late twentieth.

Chapter Twenty
Full Circle

"If man be gracious and courteous to strangers, it shows he is a citizen of the world"

§

Francis Bacon, *Essays: Of A Great Place*

My quest ended in Philippa's birthplace – Ashburton on the eastern edge of Dartmoor. But *en route* to Devon, a call from David Small diverted me to the Cotswold village of Hazelton, in a visit that left me with another mystery.

Shortly after passing through Northleach, while driving west along the A40 from Oxford to Cheltenham, I took a road leading north east through rolling countryside to Hazelton – a small, enchanting village with stupendous views across the valley towards Turkdean in the east. I drove down one hill and up another until, on the left, I saw a large complex of recently converted farm buildings – Manor Farm. Opposite was Glebe Farm, sitting slap in front of the St Andrew's Church.

I walked along the path past Glebe Farm and up a steep incline to the top of the knoll. I skirted round the church and went directly to the northwest corner of the churchyard for I was looking for a particular grave. The Victorian marker tablet was quite plain except for a bunch of flowers carved into the top and a few simple words.

Sacred to the memory of
ELIZA PRENTISE
BORN AT NEVIS, WEST INDIES
March 1st 1810
DIED AT CHELTENHAM
Feby 8th 1889
For many years a resident in this Parish
The Lord careth for the Strangers

I sat there for a long time, contemplating another stone, another country, another woman. Both lived in exceedingly turbulent times and Hazelton would have seemed as foreign to Eliza as Nevis had to Philippa – as strange as a distant planet.

The 1871 Census tells us that Eliza Prentise once lived at Manor Farm, with John Humphris and his second wife, also an Eliza, who was thirty-eight years younger than him. John, a farmer who employed twenty people, was listed as head of the household, while Eliza Prentise was listed as a boarder, unmarried, aged fifty-eight, born in Nevis, West India Isles. Her occupation was given as general domestic servant. However, we know she had already been living at Manor Farm for some time, when John's first wife Mary was alive.

Ten years later when the next census was taken, John was dead; his grave lies on the opposite side of the churchyard to Eliza's. The two women were now living together at Glebe Farm, along with Eliza Humphris's six-year-old niece, Emma Smith. Eliza Prentise, now sixty-eight, is still listed as a boarder though no occupation is given.

However, by the time of the 1891 census, Eliza was dead. Though she had been living in Cheltenham where her will was proved, for some time her links with Hazelton must have been strong for that is where she chose to be buried, in quintessential tranquil Cotswold landscape.

Yet how did she ever come to a minute village in such remote English countryside? Just as Philippa before, what force of circumstance sent her away from her birthplace? She would have been in her early twenties when the slaves were freed – given, of course, that the date of her birth on the grave is correct. The Nevisian records of that time are none too brilliant and if she was of mixed race, hers may not have been preserved at all. We don't know the true facts, though the words on her stone – *The Lord careth for the Strangers* – are intriguing and comforting suggesting that she had been well looked after. But why did she ever leave in the first place?

The reason is not difficult to fathom. Once the slaves were freed all the estates quickly collapsed. The plantation owners may eventually have received some compensation, but the catastrophic decline of the sugar industry in the twenty-seven years between the Act of Emancipation and the final Abolition left many in debt. So most of the money they received went to pay off their creditors. Then the price of land fell sharply and soon it was so dirt cheap that much was bought up as a long-term speculation by merchant firms in England and their representatives on St Kitts.

But the landowners were not the only ones affected. By the middle of the 19th century wages were half what they had been in 1807, as the pathetic price for sugar fell by a further twenty per cent. Though by 1871, when the population of Nevis was around 12,000, some sugar and molasses were still being produced, the economic decline was in full spate and even though some men, such as the Hon. Graham Briggs, were still buying up sugar estates, the crop gradually disappeared.

Such conditions, of course, also severely affected the descendants of the original slave population. Free they might be, but their immediate conditions post-Emancipation, were not substantially different from those pre-Emancipation. Many field labourers remained as apprentices for a further six years but soon the planters could no longer afford to pay even the subsistence level wages which were supposedly now available. Gradually the agriculture switched to a share-cropping system which a number of the staff at Montpelier remember well. By the middle of the century, forty of the island's eighty estates were operating a system by which each man was given two acres of land to work: some planted sugar and retained one third to one half of the crop. In almost every way the mid nineteenth century was a very hard time and many Nevisians left to find work elsewhere – in the Caribbean or in Europe. Clearly Eliza was amongst them. However, we have no record of when she actually left Nevis but if this was shortly before she turned up in Hazelton, this would be in the mid 1860s – a time of the greatest distress on Nevis.

How she ended up in Hazelton is equally a mystery. Since her occupation in the Census is given as a domestic servant, the likeliest place for her to have worked is at Salperton Park – a large country house about a mile north of the village, linked by a direct and easy footpath. The house was probably owned by the family of James Browne around 1880, and we know that Brownes were plantation owners on Nevis and St Kitts from the 17th century onwards. That is fact, yet Eliza Prentise's connection with their Cotswold estate is speculative.

Eliza, who was buried in Hazelton on February 13th 1887 aged 78, composed an intriguing will. This doesn't suggest she was poor at all for she left significant amounts of money and shares to various friends. Eliza Humphrey received three hundred pounds, and all her wearing apparel and the ornaments in her trunk. Emma Smith received one hundred pounds and the bedroom furniture, a leather writing desk and a counterpane that her benefactor had made. To her friends Ann Dixon and Emma Dixon, of Haverley in the county of Devon, she left shares in the London Chartered Bank of Australia

§

Finally I arrived in Ashburton. My nephew, Martin, and his wife, Liz, who live in Tavistock, drove me across the superb scenery of Dartmoor, where sylvan views can suddenly yield to cold granite starkness and dangerous, unforgiving weather. Though the tin mine industry had long since gone, Martin showed me several remnants – towers and concealed mine entrances.

I decided to meet Geraldine Bews, who had been helping with the research, in St Andrews Church, which had been there in Philippa's time. The well, where one New Year's Day Philippa tried to catch the rays of the rising sun, had long gone, but the general layout of the old town is easily identifiable. One can still walk – as she did – along North Street, then west along the riverbank to where her cottage might have been, and return to East Street via the old Shameface Lane. I bought a pewter mug from the antique shop and Robert Prideaux's *Old Ashburton* from a bookshop. We discussed at length what Geraldine had found in the documents and how serious were the gaps in the record. David Webb, a local historian, briefed me about Ashburton in mediaeval times and especially about the plague. We were all in no doubt that Philippa started life at the very bottom of the heap.

Over a beer and sandwich in a pub at some idyllic spot on the moor, I talked with Martin and Liz about the mystery that had so obsessed me and how it remained as much a puzzle about Roland Archibald as about Philippa. While still searching for explanations about Roland Archibald's words spoken twenty years ago, I was helped by two fresh facts. By now, I knew that when we first met he was much older than I thought, and this fact gave greater significance to the words he spoke at the tomb.

The second fact was that on my last two visits to Nevis I had met his daughter, Mrs Judith McGrath, now in her mid 70s. Not only had she given me much detail about the family but she also confirmed her father's wish to be buried alongside Philippa. She believed I was the only person outside the family to whom he had said this. She spoke of her father with a mixture of great affection and sad exasperation at the way events played out.

Judith had once lived in Jamaica, but she had returned to look after Roland in his final years. Though her own home was now on St Kitts, she had children and grandchildren still on Nevis.

The Archibalds were an established and successful family. Roland's father, Alexander, a merchant, had several profitable commercial properties in both Charlestown and St Kitts. He had five sons and four daughters whom he brought up single-handedly after his wife died. Roland, his second child, was the only one not to go into business. He studied agriculture and though he eventually was an *estater*, it was his father who initially bought the Saddle Hill lands.

She showed me a survey of his land drawn in 1879 that used to hang on the wall of Roland's house on Saddle Hill and luckily survived the hurricane. The boundaries were clearly specified with Prentis Works forming the western ones.

Alexander's acquisitions were extensive: in 1931 he purchased 150 acres of Stock Pen; in 1940 he gave Roland three estates – Macfarlane's to the east, Doctor's Bottom below Saddle Hill and Morton Hill, a little to the west. In 1944, however, Roland himself purchased Upper and Lower Prentis from two people in St Kitts. Though times were not good, his acreage was huge and he survived reasonably well.

During World War 2, Roland was in Jamaica. When he returned to Nevis he lived first in Charlestown, then in 1971 began building the house on Saddle Hill. Judith insisted that none of his children could understand why, and if the truth be told, they didn't like it up there. They felt the place was strange and desolate, yet for some reason they could not fathom – possibly the death of his wife – their father became something of a hermit and didn't welcome any strangers. His son told me that if he felt you were intruding he could have met you not with a glass of cold water in his hand, but a gun. Nevertheless, despite his reputation as a tough man, he was also regarded as a very fair one.

With the help of his brother who lived in America, Roland eventually revived his old cattle business. He bought two hundred animals and aimed to supply fresh milk on a regular basis first to the hospital and then to the whole island. To begin with, things went well and he reached his first goal. But he never got anywhere near the second, because as Judith said, *'it all went cock-eyed'*.

There were bitter, jealous rivalries, disputes about land and rights, envy following his success with the milk business. Some of his cows were driven into salt pans; some stolen in a spate of cattle rustling; others just upped and died. Yet though the business eventually failed, cows turned out to be very significant, for thanks to them he discovered Philippa, and thanks to her made some sort of peace with himself in the last years of his life.

The cattle on Nevis do not range freely but are tethered to heavy stones with strong rope, long enough for adequate daily grazing. One day, Roland Archibald saw that one of his cows was tied to a broken stone that looked unusual. He told his man to tie the cow to a rock, then propped the odd piece up against a tree and gently began cleaning. Soon he realised he had part of a marker tablet and started to search for the other piece. With the most unbelievable good fortune, he found it and when he placed the two together they matched. After three centuries it was surprising that the broken pieces of tablet had survived at all.

I believe that reading the inscription had to be one of the most moving moments of his life. Here is a man in his mid seventies, who knows he is ill with cancer. He owns land called Prentis Works and on it finds an ancient tablet commemorating the life of a woman with the same name, who lived not 20, not 50, but 300 years before and who worked the same land.

Since he was constructing a cistern he now ordered spare stone and built a tomb on a knoll way above his house, where the view was spectacular. He aligned the marker tablet in the traditional east-west direction, with the head pointing towards the setting sun. He believed that short of a massive earthquake or volcanic eruption, nothing would disturb Philippa's memorial. Even when Hurricane Hugo destroyed his house there was no damage to the tomb whatsoever.

Every day he came up to talk to Philippa, for he had already decided to be buried alongside her. He sought permission from the authorities and this was granted. However, shortly before he died the government withdrew their consent and Roland was very upset. Then he had to go to Jamaica for aggressive radiation treatment, but soon died and was buried there.

I asked Judith whether Philippa's skeleton was inside the tomb. She was adamant that not only were there no bones inside, but her father hadn't even searched for them. She insisted that if a skeleton had been found not only would he have told her, but everyone in Cox Village would have known too. There was absolutely nothing inside the tomb that Roland built.

Nevertheless not only is there is a pervasive skeleton myth about Philippa and the tomb, but there's a money myth too. Judith reports that many people believe Roland was very rich and all his treasure is in there. If only, she adds ruefully. But her father wasn't wealthy at all especially once the cattle business had collapsed.

Yet the myths persist. One lady who claimed certain spiritual powers, went up to Saddle Hill carrying a crystal attached on the end of a string, whose movement would reveal what was in the tomb. I was present and, of course, the crystal moved as she predicted it would. So she stated definitively that Philippa's body was indeed inside and wanted everyone to know she was very happy.

Not only is that story not true, but it doesn't *have* to be true, for the story is perfect as it stands. All of us who have investigated the mystery of the tomb and its ancient marker tablet, like to think of Philippa resting peacefully somewhere in Lower Prentis, most possibly near where Marco has excavated. Not only do we *like* to think so, but actually *believe* it to be so.

Yet the initial fact that so tantalised me, remains unexplained. Here was a man speaking with devotion about a woman whose descendants likely owned his ancestors as slaves. As in all other places, the slave trade on Nevis was vile and abhorrent with horrendous injustices and terrible brutalities. Nevertheless, I have to say that during the twenty-five years I have been visiting Nevis, I have met very little anti-white anger — unlike on St Thomas and Puerto Rico. So possibly the absence of bitterness in Roland Archibald — that mirrors Nelson Mandela's magnificent attitude — is typical throughout the island.

Other aspects form part of any explanation. Roland was eighty-four when I met him and he knew he hadn't long to live. Four years later Hurricane Hugo struck. His children rang regularly while the storm raged, insisting that he go down to Charlestown, but he refused. He was lucky to survive for the house was slap in the hurricane's path. But the destruction of his house marked the end of his dream.

Though it's far too easy to romanticise the man, the words he spoke clearly reflected a deeply held emotion. What did Philippa really mean to him? Two things I think: first, she had created not only the estate which he now owned — and which he, too, would leave to the next generation — but also the country of Nevis – his country. So they were linked by that mutual effort, one so lasting that of course they could rest side by side. Their lives might have been separated by three hundred years, but what is three hundred years when measured against eternity?

Secondly, Roland Archibald was deeply religious and likely believed he might well go to the same eternity as Philippa. So talking to her every day mitigated the pain of his own mortality and the life he was leaving.

But why do people today still trek up to talk to Philippa? They have a variety of reasons and beliefs, but amongst many personal ones they mentioned to me, one was common. History is a consoling subject and through history we touch the past and restore it to life. Philippa's story is humanity's story.

§

Without doubt, those are uplifting conclusions. But as we sat on Dartmoor and Martin and Liz quizzed me, I had to admit that there are still very many gaps in my reconstruction. The most serious relate to Clement. There is no doubt that he and Philippa lived together on Nevis. But in contrast with Philippa, I have not found one single document that allows me to say that this man, born on this date, lived in this town, left England on this ship in this year, came to Nevis and married Philippa Stephens of Ashburton, on this date. Indeed I have found only one document from the right period that even gives the same name – a *'quit claim by Clement Prentis to Richard Pretyman on property in Suffolk, June 21 1634'.*

However, a Clement Prentis does appear in an American family tree set out by Linus Dewald Jnr. Baptised in April 1569, he was the son of Francis Prentis of Stock Ash. In 1606 he married Elisabeth Wilcock of North Ockenden in Essex, just north of the modern Dartford Tunnel. He was still alive in 1617 and had a sister called Eleanor. Since the names of the towns in this reference – Braysworth and Thornham – are on the Suffolk/Norfolk border and are the same as on the quit claim, he could be related to the Clement Prentis on the quit claim. Several Prentises with their names spelt all and every way, can be traced in America.

Although there were many Prentises in East Anglia — and still are — Clement has not turned up in any of the shipping records, or on the Oaths of Allegiance, or any other record. However, David Small says this is not surprising, for anyone going to the West Indies could just have boarded a ship in Ipswich without fuss. A friend of mine, who lives in East Anglia, told me about his ancestor who simply walked down to the estuary one day and took the next ship out — and it didn't call in London. So if Clement already was a planter on Nevis when Philippa arrived, he sailed before registrations were compulsory and his movements would go unrecorded.

As a result of these facts — or lack of them — and given the gaps in Philippa's records, I have to challenge myself. Could I stand up in a court of law and say that I have proved beyond reasonable doubt that Philippa Stephens, spinster of Ashburton, aged 28 or thereabouts, actually is the Philippa who married Clement Prentis and is buried on Saddle Hill? The answer is no, I could not.

However, the balance of probability indicates that certainly it has to be her, even though many who have read this story have raised the following objection: if she is the original Philippa Stephens, she lived to a surprisingly ripe and highly unlikely old age for that time. It may be highly unlikely, but it doesn't follow that this didn't occur. We have documentary evidence that two of the women sailing on the same ship from Dartmouth, also lived into their seventies. Judith Stephens, baptised in Plymouth in 1610, died on 23rd August 1687 in Roxbury, Suffolk, Massachusetts. Margarett Harwood, baptised 1612 in Stoke Gabriel, Devon, who married William Hawkins on 13th July 1635, died in Providence, Rhode Island in the same decade as Judith.

We know too, that in the eighteenth century, four of Philippa's female descendants lived into their seventies, so the family carried a longevity gene. In those days the crucial years for survival were the first five years of life — as they are in many developing countries now. Along with poverty and malnutrition, add polio, diphtheria, measles, whooping cough, tuberculosis and malaria and many infants are taken out at an early age. But if they survive, their immune system is in good shape. If in addition, you also survived the plague at Ashburton in your twenties, you must have been tenaciously strong. Thus I don't think Philippa's age is a really valid objection.

There is, however, a more serious objection. When Geraldine Bews was checking on Philippa's parents she found not only their wedding entry and Philippa's birth certificate, as well as the Poor Relief payments made to the family by the Ashburton Overseers, but she also ran across a certificate for a wedding between a Philippa Stephens and a Stephen Weeks. Nevertheless, Geraldine believes that the Philippa Stephens who took the Oath of Allegiance in Dartmouth, really was born in Ashburton and did actually sail for St. Christopher. The second Philippa Stephens entry could either refer to someone born outside of Ashburton, or the name recorded was possibly a clerical error made by the scribes. Whatever, as the tombstone testifies, a Philippa certainly went to Nevis.

The final gaps in my reconstruction are the most frustrating of all. Unlike many famous women in the seventeenth century – Mary, Queen of Scots, or Queen Elizabeth I – nothing is written about Philippa in any documents and there are no portraits. I don't know what she looked like, what she said, how she reacted in anger or in love. I cannot 'hear' Philippa's voice at all. Thus, though the events I describe in the middle section of this book really did take place, the conversations are inevitably imaginary.

So who was Philippa Prentis Philipps? She was a tough, ordinary, extremely poor woman who lived an extraordinary life and defeated all the odds. She was not a famous woman in history and though she helped to create a country, she didn't change her society at all. Yet she witnessed and experienced many remarkable events.

However, at the end of this absorbing quest I know at least one thing with absolute certainty. The hole in the top of Philippa's tablet, that David, Brett and I all noticed, did not once hold a decoration but had been knocked out by a herdsman who needed to tether a cow.

Yet as I approach the age that Roland Archibald was when I first met him, I know, just as surely, that there is no ending, for through our descendants the story continues. As long as there are human beings on this earth – whose experiences reflect love and pain, hopes and fears, ecstasy and tragedy – rivers of time will flow for them just as they did for Roland and Philippa. So other chroniclers can take inspiration from ordinary lives lived well – outside of the spotlight which focuses only on famous winners, or desperate losers, or just the noisiest.

Chapter Twenty One
The Wash of History: a Retrospect

"You never finish a novel. People just take them away from you."

§

Phillip Roth

As the months pass, fresh fragments from history continue to appear. Some are remarkable, some moving, all precious contributions to the jigsaw. Many came from Roland Archibald's descendants in both America and Nevis. I came to know his grandchildren on the island and grieved with them, when one, Brian Mills, lost his life in the Atlantic waters off Nevis — yet another reminder that the Caribbean holds danger as well beauty. In January 2010, when I spoke to the Nevis Historical & Conservation Society, a shy, polite, sixteen-year-old boy introduced himself as Roland's great grandson.

One of the most valuable nuggets arrived in lengthy emails from Bill Stancliff of Boston, and Bob and Sherry Stancliff who live in Cincinnati, USA, for they turned my hunch into a truth. After I had learnt that the stone for Philippa's marker tablet came from either Hurricane Hill or Cade's Bay, and it would have been carved in Jamestown — the capital of Nevis in 1683 — I tried to identify the carver. The only stonemason I could find was the craftsman, James Stanclift, who had sailed from England in September 1680, on *The Nevis Merchant*. Yet he was listed as an indentured servant — a surprising status since during the latter part of the 17th century, their numbers dropped significantly as the use of slaves increased.

So yet another fresh question has to be answered: why did he carry this status? His family, Nonconformists in Shibden Valley, Yorkshire, were imprisoned for allowing the Rev. Oliver Heywood, to hold outlawed religious services in their home. If James had been caught up in the current religious and political turmoil it is possible that he had been forced to go to Nevis as an indentured servant. In fact it is likely, for at that time, no one voluntarily sought that grade.

Having examined my photographs, Bill, Bob and Sherry quickly became convinced that indeed it was their ancestor who had carved Philippa's marker tablet. Over the years they had visited Nevis many times, seeking examples of his work during meticulous searches. The ruins of Jamestown were beneath the waters, so there was nothing to see there, but they looked in all the other obvious places such as old churchyards and their gravestones. Yet they had no reason whatsoever, to have trekked to one of the most isolated locations on Nevis, in the expectation of finding James's work. But now they were able to send me firm evidence as to why my deduction had been correct. They wrote:

"A stone carver's letters and style are as distinctive as the handwriting of a scrivener. Despite the fact that one of the features of James Stanclift's signature lettering was missing on Philippa's tablet, there are a great many others that identify his work, present on that tablet." They then listed fifteen characteristics common to Stanclift's carvings in America and those on her marker stone.

Other fascinating artefacts came not from the land, but the sea floor — relics not so much of Philippa's life, as of the persistent conflicts with the French. On 25th February 1782 – the first day of the Battle of Frigate Bay – the 28 gun frigate, *HMS Solebay*, a signal and supply vessel, was lost half a mile off the southwest coast of Nevis. She was carrying 160 barrels of gunpowder and while maintaining her proper position, grounded in waters some fifteen to twenty feet deep. When the French ships began firing into this sitting target, Captain Charles H. Everett realised his situation was impossible and ordered his crew to abandon ship, and to keep her out of French hands, set the vessel on fire. She burnt for about an hour then blew up in a huge explosion, which in the words of a witness, "*...reverberated from the mountain like distent thunder.*"

Early in 2010, a naval chart from 1808 was discovered, which showed the position of the wreck. Using the 31-foot boat of the Nevis Air and Seaport Authority, seven people, including Vince Hubbard, started to search. They tried underwater radar first, but the boat's power supply was too weak. So they reverted to low-tech: and slowly towed their two best divers behind the boat.

Within fifteen minutes, a large iron cannon was sighted, and a few minutes later two more appeared. Thus far they have found twelve cannon, a number of iron ballast bars, a length of chain and other artefacts that clearly identify the wreck as the Solebay.

They hope that the Nevis Government will designate the site as a protected park and permit regulated diving. Then, in 2011, they plan to establish an underwater archaeology school. Though it might be too much to hope that other examples of Stanclift's carvings will be found, yet, if eventually, the sunken ruins of Jamestown are systematically searched, then who knows? Relics from Philippa's time may well appear.

As each puzzle solved prompts further questions, and others take possession of this tale, nevertheless the central conviction underpinning my quest has not altered one iota. The course of history is never solely determined by those in high, influential positions – whether they be the great and the good, or the tyrannical and authoritarian. Professional spin doctors work very hard to have us believe this – especially at election times – and too often we do. The television critic, A.A.Gill was dismissive when he wrote (The Sunday Times, 25th September, 2010): *"the common people are merely the noises off of history. The problem with people's history is that while it's worthy, it's also quite boring and repetitive."*

Yet our human chronicles cannot be contained in such a simplistic way. Tolstoy understood this very clearly as scenes from *War & Peace* illustrate. The evening before the Battle of Borodino, when the generals led by Kutuzov are 'planning' the battle, the philosophical Pierre Bezukhov meets the professional soldier, Prince Andrei Bolkhonsky. The generals might just as well go to bed, for these two younger men agree that, actually, the outcome will be determined by the individual actions of ordinary people. During the battle next day, as Pierre wanders across the field of deathly destruction, their conviction is vividly and violently confirmed.

Similarly, though the development of the Caribbean clearly had a great deal to do with the decisions of people thousands of miles away – Charles I, Oliver Cromwell and the merchants in London who financed the ventures – whose artefacts, as Gill insists, have a unique beauty and grandeur – how Nevis evolved was ultimately determined by the daily actions of ordinary, unknown people such as Clement Prentis and his wife. Not that Philippa ever gave this any conscious thought – for whether a poor woman in Ashburton or a comfortably-off estator in Nevis, she just worked hard, lived her life well and hoped to go to heaven.

During the arduous process of piecing together the shreds of evidence scavenged in the Caribbean and in Great Britain, more than three hundred years after Philippa died, my life and hers fused. Yet clearly I had never realised this and it took exhausting discussions with Richard Friedhoff, a long term friend, before I faced this fact. I had found inspiration in Philippa, as she took form in my imagination. The observer affected the observed: so we changed each other and the demarcations of centuries and time dissolved.

Actually it was three dear friends, Edna Healey, Richard Friedhoff and Justin Hardy, who from the very start appreciated the significance – greatness even – of a life completely lost in the wash of history. If undertaken for all the women similarly forgotten, my determination to resurrect Philippa may well have been presumptuous and hubristic, yet in the end, all three, bless them, insisted that it was worth every effort.

Richard summed up their shared conviction perfectly.

"Our present world has prospered from a rigid view of time, cause and effect and progress – a view ridiculed by certain other civilizations. Yet something has truly been lost in the spiritual disconnection with our ancestors. In focusing so totally on the present, we forget that we are historical actors expressing precedents that we feel – that animate us – but that we cannot see. The world itself has had a long and largely unseen history to which any given generation can only react. So one can genuinely ask: are not people who live so totally in the present, who are concerned with only what can be seen and measured, in fact blinding themselves to far greater possibilities?"

The End

References

Bridenbaugh, Carl & Roberta. *No peace beyond the line* 1624-1690. *The English in the Caribbean* (OUP 1972) (deals with the early settlements in the West Indies, mostly with the Leeward Islands).

Harlow, V.T. (ed) *Colonising Expeditions to the West Indies and the Guiana [sic] 1623-1667* The Hakluyt Society, London, 1923. The early voyages of exploration are covered, including those of Sir Henry Colt, as well as accounts of the settlements in Barbados and St Kitts.

Hotten, John Camden (ed) *The Original Lists of Persons of Quality; Emigrants; Religious Exiles; Political Rebels; Serving Men Sold for a Term of Years; Apprentices; Children Stolen; Maidens Pressed; and Others who went from Great Britain to the American Plantations 1600-1700* (London: Chatto & Windus, 1874).

Hubbard, Vincent K. *Swords, Ships & Sugar: History of Nevis*. Premiere Editions International Inc., Oregon. 1992.

Ligon, Richard. *A True & Exact History of the Island of Barbados, 1647-1650* (London 1657). One of the few contemporary accounts.

Olwig, Karen Fog. *Global Culture, Island Identity: Continuity and Change in the Afro-Caribbean Community of Nevis*. Harvard Academic Publishers, 1993.

Prideaux, Robert P.F., Sparke Amery (ed) *Old Ashburton: Being Recollections of Master Robert Prideaux* (Attorney-at-law) 1509-1569, (Totnes: T & A Mortimore, 1882).

Russell, Percy. *Dartmouth* (Bournemouth: Batsford Books 1950).

Watts, David. *The West Indies: Patterns of Development, Culture & Environmental Change since 1492*. Cambridge University Press, 1987.

Details of the Compensation Claims can be found in the National Archives, documents CO243/1-9; CO243/5 deal with those arising from the French Invasion. Documents PRO T71/364; T71/366; T71/367; T71/368 (the one that lists Clement Phillip Prentis) and T71/369 deal with those following the Abolition of Slavery.